MANAGEMENT OF DEER AND THEIR HABITAT
Principles and Methods

by

A.J. DE NAHLIK

with a foreword

by

LORD RAMSAY

Wilson Hunt

First published 1992 by
Wilson Hunt,
Stourton View, East Stour,
Gillingham, Dorset SP8 5JZ

British Library Cataloguing-in-Publication Data

de Nahlik, A.J.
  Management of Deer and their Habitat :
  Principles and Methods
  I. Title
  636.294

  ISBN 0 907519 01 6
  ISBN 0 907519 02 4 Pbk

By the same Author:

Wild Deer (Faber and Faber, 1959)
Deer Management (David and Charles, 1974)
Wild Deer (Ashford Press, 1987) 2nd Edition.

Produced and typeset in Times by Wilson Hunt
Printed and bound in Great Britain by
Butler & Tanner Ltd, Frome and London

Contents

Part 3: Deer Economics

Appendices

Plates

Figures

Foreword

by

The Lord Ramsay
President of the British Deer Society

Wild deer are an integral part of our countryside. There are several hundreds of thousands in Britain yet few are ever seen by the public for, quite rightly, they are wary of man, their predator. Deer eat and scar trees and damage crops so they are not always the object of man's devotion, especially the farmer and forester.

The more we study and learn about deer in their environment the better able we are to understand how to live with them, limit the damage they do and manage them as a valuable and beautiful asset rather than as vermin. The study of deer, or any wild species for that matter, requires a broad and often detailed understanding of their habitat which varies so much throughout the British Isles.

This is Andrew de Nahlik's fourth book on deer. It is a result of many years of experience as a stalker, deer manager and advisor on deer matters in England and Scotland. There are very few people with his breadth of experience over such a period of time.

He has written this book for anybody with an interest in deer, but his objective is to prove that properly planned and managed woodlands, with well managed deer (and game for that matter), can produce significant annual revenue, whilst the capital gain from forestry is maturing. The book is packed with information and ideas. Some of his ideas in his earlier works have become accepted, others are controversial and have stimulated many discussions in various circles. Without doubt this book with more new concepts will also give rise to much discussion.

Whatever one's opinions, this work contributes to the furthering of understanding of deer and their habitat, both being our heritage; it should be read therefore by all those who want to improve their knowledge of deer and how they can and should be allowed to fit into our plans for the countryside along with the other interests of man and nature.

Dalhousie Lodge
Edzell
Angus

Ramsay.

From the Author

From the days of *Wild Deer* published by Faber and Faber in 1959, most of my writing effort has been concentrated on deer management, economics of deer and the owners' attitude to managing deer. Since these days many other authors have also addressed the issue of modern deer management and in essence many of the principles which we have suggested have become accepted practice.

In recent years I have become concerned over the deterioration of the hill, the home of the Scottish red deer. Increasingly in areas of high populations of red deer and indeed of sheep, heather became browner, with less flower in the glorious Scottish autumn; the new flower bearing growth being diligently devoured by deer and sheep and not only deer suffered but also grouse.

During the same period we have also seen that Britain is no longer a home to just three species of deer, red, fallow and roe. Increasingly sika are spreading and regrettably hybridising with red deer, the muntjac population is growing alarmingly and both are now reaching the Border Regions. The breeding propensity of Chinese water deer is such that sooner or later we may also see them spread. Furthermore, whilst much debate surrounds the Scottish hill red deer, little has been done to rationalise deer management in the original habitat of deer, the forest, be it in Scotland or England.

It is becoming increasingly clear that we must broaden our thinking from concentrating on deer alone to the habitat in which deer (and other wildlife) live. We must concentrate more on the protection of that habitat otherwise a day may well come when deer will suffer – either their habitat will become too poor to sustain them, or we, the humans, will become so disenchanted with deer on account of damage that a new bout of deer-hostile attitude will grow.

Two other phenomena have recently come into consideration.

Some years ago field sports came under the economic pressure of estate survival. It started with fishing and gamebird shooting and stalking followed; by now all three have seen a large degree of commercialisation to at least pay their way, ideally to bring net income. Under this pressure venison soon found its market and a price level, but stalking for sport (including trophy), has been, and still is, largely looking for an equitable price level, with many estates not realising their full income potential, possibly by a very wide margin.

Today also, field-sports, and among them deer stalking, fall under microscopic, if emotional, scrutiny of various bodies with political, ideological and other interests. Many are increasingly hostile to the traditions and practices of field sports, using the guise of a variety of sentiments.

Both these pressures make it increasingly obvious that field sports and associated interests can only survive and thrive within the orbit of rational, economically and ecologically sound management, necessitating the use of wildlife as an asset.

It was for this reason that this book started life in a script entitled "Deer and Forestry", where I was suggesting that deer, properly managed within their natural woodland habitat, and with that habitat geared to accommodate and recognise deer as a secondary product, both could coexist in an interesting and fruitful symbiosis.

The issue of land management and with it management of deer is of increasing importance. We are planning nationally to increase woodland cover of Britain by one hundred percent by the middle of the next century. In this vast undertaking deer will migrate and colonise the new deer friendly habitats. These new forests will have to be planned to allow for the impact of deer, as well as for increasing risk of road traffic accidents attributable to deer. And yet, among the seats of higher education from which future land use planners will come, deer management as a subject is ignored. For this reason I decided to restructure "Deer and Forestry" and attempt to present the basics of deer and habitat management on which the reader can build.

* * *

I have largely benefited from the significant number of authoritative works which have been published in this country, following the experience and practice of management and backed by much research which has been carried out. I had to rely, however, also on non-British sources where I could find no published British material. I acknowledge, therefore, that this book would have never come to fruition had it not been for the tremendous help, support and advice (often bitterly critical) from the many authors, publishers, friends, acquaintances, and complete strangers with similar interests, as well as from business and official circles both here and abroad.

My grateful thanks go therefore to many; the publishers and authors who allowed me to use their material: Messrs Batsford, Paul Parey Verlag-Hamburg, Neuman-Neudam – Berlin, Deutscher Jagschutz Verband, the Red Deer Commission and the Forestry Commission. I would like to acknowledge especially the vast help given in preparation of "Deer and Forestry", by Dr. Hugh Insely, who advised and edited the early draft and Dr. Philip Ratcliffe who wrote a critique on it (both are from the Forestry Commission); to Dr. Peter Hudson of the Game Conservancy Grouse Research, who read the original draft and gave some very useful advice. Special thanks go to Professor Egon Wagenknecht who allowed me to use material from his *Rotwild*; indeed, I also have to acknowledge that I have used that work in my updated and extended edition of *Wild Deer*, doing so before the question of copyright in relation to works originating in Eastern Europe applied. In putting together the final draft, my gratitude must be extended to many: to the Institute of Terrestial Ecology for permission to use their deer distribution maps produced by the Records Centre, from records supplied by the British Deer Society and the Mammals Society, to Dr. Archie McDiarmid, who authored the original disease appendix as used in *Wild Deer* (1987) and Mr. Peter Dalton who helped in its final re-editing for this work, also Mr. Hugh Rose and the Ministry of Defence for the use of photographs in this section; to friends from Wessex Branch of the British Deer Society from the Branch Chairman Robert Underhill, who helped with many forestry aspects and edited the early script, to the members of the Branch Committee who rallied to a call for photographs, especially Ray and Anne Hobbs, Roger and Dorothy Ireland and Paul Yates, and to John Willett, also a member of the Wessex Branch. I am also most grateful to the two BDS Committees – Education and Training, who allowed me to use their material, as well as the Chairman of the Society, Mr. Hugh Oliver-Bellasis for his help and the Lord Ramsay, the President, for writing the Foreword. I would also like to acknowledge and thank *Stalking Magazine*, who published several articles on subjects, at the time topical, which in a similar or identical form appear in this work.

And finally my gratitude has to go to my wife for her life-long support and with regard to this book, not only drawing many illustrations and designing the cover but also for tirelessly and patiently reading and correcting the many drafts. Last but not least I am most grateful to Mr. Michael Baxter Brown who agreed to read and edit the proofs and without affecting the idiosyncrasies of my style of writing, made the book more readable.

A.J. de N.
March 1992

Part One

The Principles

1.1. Background

O F THE species of deer living in Britain in the wild today, two are indigenous, red and roe deer. Roe deer, in fact, although indigenous, were on the brink of extinction by the early 19th century and were re-introduced in South–West England. Fallow deer have inhabited Britain since Roman days probably having been introduced by the Romans as a source of food.

A common characteristic to all three of these is that by nature they are woodland dwellers and the change in afforestation has also resulted in some changes in the character of the deer population. The natural deer woodland is a deciduous one surrounded by fields, grazing and cultivated, providing a reasonable amount of easy to obtain, and nutritious food. Such are the vagaries of Nature that of the three species of woodland deer, one, the red deer, having found itself without forest after the disappearance of the Caledonian Forest in Scotland became, reasonably happily, a moorland–hill dweller.

The other three species, sika, muntjac and Chinese water deer (CWD) are comparatively recent additions to the 'wild' fauna of Britain. Their colonisation is attributed to either escapes from large deer parks like Woburn, which sported all three in captivity, or releases into the wild by owners keen on stalking, as in the case of sika's introduction to Scotland. In fact, the appearance of muntjac and Chinese water deer in Bedfordshire in 1950 is without a doubt linked to the Woburn Abbey collection and Whipsnade Zoo.

Ever since the dawn of commercial forests the feed platform for deer has been undergoing a transformation. Many of the nutritious and palatable plants found in the old 'wild' forest, which was basically deciduous or mixed self-regenerating, were vanishing. The new commercial forests of close-planted conifers not only changed the face of the countryside but also denied deer and other wildlife species the assurance of the past choice. The newly introduced species of trees and with them the structure of the vegetation of the undergrowth presented in many respects a less attractive feeding platform to deer. The exception were tree plantations, abounding in tasty and nutritious food. Basically, however, these changes forced the deer to either alter their feeding habits, including perhaps a higher reliance on new plants as the food

1

source, or seek new and more friendly habitats.

In consequence the feeding pressure may have been directed at vegetation which was previously a low grade choice. It now became a choice *par force*, or *par force* caused deer migration or even elimination of species. Of course this is a gross generalisation. Some species of deer were more affected than others, sika for instance found the new conifer habitat quite acceptable and have done well in some areas heavily afforested with conifers; other deer often preferred to seek pastures new, with richer feeding.

For many years of modern afforestation concern over the welfare of wildlife was minimal and the understanding of what wildlife generally, and deer specifically, require of the habitat was almost non-existent. It was not understood, for instance, that plantations of young trees were vulnerable to damage, and that these appearing in large acreages, often bordering on older timber stands, provided an attractive food source to deer. One could say, therefore, that where there appeared propensity by deer of 'addressing' valuable plants of the forest it was, more usually than not, of the foresters' own making. It was in 1959 that I advised the need to provide facilities for deer and their culling[1] and other writers followed. For a long time, however, there was a marked resistance to the inclusion of wildlife facilities in forest planning; what advice was published, based on the experience of other countries, called for the sacrifice of some land for non-crop planting since it was deemed necessary that it should be re-researched in Britain before introduction could be contemplated. Not until the last 15 or 20 years have real attempts been made to create a deer and wildlife friendly habitat within the forest. It is not suggested here that the change was solely for the benefit of deer and wildlife; there was a general lobby forming against large plantations of conifers offering little to the beauty of the countryside, unsuitable for leisure activities even as basic as trekking and walking, and bringing havoc to wildlife in general.

A better understanding of the environment, political pressure for the conservation of wildlife and the growth of interest in the countryside among a large proportion of the population have all resulted in enforcement of new, more progressive, regimes. With this movement came also the widening of the fields of study not only at the departments of environmental studies at universities but also introducing a more outward approach to hitherto introspective thinking in studies of agriculture, estate management, forestry and similar. Again, however, one could detect that it was not all purely for the benefit of wildlife, deer or game.

The interest in wildlife included the interest of a section of the population in country sports. To a large extent it was the agriculture and

---

[1] de Nahlik, A.J., *Wild Deer* (Faber & Faber 1959).

forestry industries that were providing facilities for at least two of these, game shooting and deer stalking, sports which landowners realised could be sources of significant revenue from sportsmen, whilst the market offered a good income from game and venison dealers, who, in the mid 1960s identified a hungry export market on the Continent.

The opportunities created by the industrialisation of the countryside were first noted by the water authorities who, when planning new water reservoirs, included in their plans facilities for water sports from sailing to fishing, bringing quick and significant yearly revenue return on capital invested.

Of course the change-over from the old introspective education, and the old habits of shooting and stalking purely for sport and pleasure was not easy. Even today education in the management of deer and game is scanty. Landowners found the change from treating their sport as 'fun' to an economically viable proposition was often a bitter pill to swallow; their choice was simple however – no longer were their estates able to subsidise sport and the continuation of sport depended on it being made at least self-supporting.

1.2. Distribution and Migration

THERE WAS a fashion in most of the countries of Europe for owners of large estates with parks to adorn their parks with deer. These were in the main red and fallow, with a few going for the more exotic species. The parks were fenced, and earlier walled, but it is conceivable that neither of these protective measures were fully and always deer proof, so deer managed to escape.

The fashions of the Victorian and post-Victorian field sporting practices aided the spread and proliferation of deer. In the first place the style of game shooting led many estates to planting small woodlands as game coverts; these were followed by belts of trees over which to drive game to guns. Both provided good cover and feed not only for game birds but also deer, especially fallow and roe. There was another fashion, however, which led to the esteem in which especially red but also fallow deer were held – that of deer stalking and adorning the walls of family homes with antlered heads, either stuffed or just skulls mounted on shields.

This interest in trophy hunting was, and still is, common over many parts of the world. Its consequence in some places was, and is, the deterioration of the quality of game animals; the best and strongest being taken out as trophies often well before they reach their prime and manage to breed. Not only did trophies as decoration become fashionable, but equally attractive in some circles was the fact that the 'lucky' hunters found their names in reviews of 'hunting' achievements published from time to time in the sporting and other press, and even in books.

Trophy hunting has its rightful place in the management of deer and other wild game. But these are the trophies of old, quality beasts which have lived their full life span, passed their qualities to their progeny and are ultimately taken as the 'harvest' instead of being allowed to die of old age.

The same period that gave style to deer stalking in Scotland led to the lending of the Royal Ear to an interest in deer which has lasted until the present day among members of the Royal Family. The interest that spread not only increased the numbers of people who stalked but also encompassed other species of deer following red deer in becoming quarry. As the trophies on the walls rose in numbers, the hill and woodland was

4

growing short of good mature males, and females proliferated.

Over the years the walls which surrounded the parks and contained the park deer fell into a state of disrepair, especially during the two World Wars; in many instances, deer escaped.

The progress and changes in technology characteristic of this century and especially the two wars has led to changes in agricultural practices. Gone were the unproductive headland hedges and small fields – in came prairie farming, mechanised tending of fields and agrochemical aids to productivity.

The tragedy of the first part of this century, especially post-World War I and until the early 1950s, was that all deer came to be regarded by some at best as a trophy, and at worst by many, as pest and vermin, especially in the woodlands. As trophies, all species throughout the country were stalked by a few, as vermin they were snared, trapped, variously shot, including during bird drives, usually with pellets of the same size as used for partridges and rabbits. When they were shot with shotguns many were wounded, often mortally. No one regarded deer as a natural asset.

In the post-war years, members of the Forces and the Civil Service have been introduced to deer stalking on the Continent and started forming sporting and political pressure groups. They called for protective legislation and limitation of the weapon systems used in deer stalking. The position of deer did not improve, however, until the introduction of the first deer legislation in the 1950s and early '60s.

It is in this way that in many parts of Britain not only the interest in deer increased, but that deer, hitherto almost unnoticed, have been 'discovered' as existing in many contained pockets of land where a supportive habitat for them exists.

The stalking sportsmen however, were inclined to look for and find their stalking and were more than happy to shoot a few bucks or stags every year. Very few, if any, addressed the question of female deer which, unculled, gave rise to a fast growth of the deer population. As the density of deer in various localities increased and the pressure on feeding grew, so deer started to move out and colonise new locations. The programmes of afforestation undertaken by private individuals, companies, local and central government attracted and facilitated such migration, and deer started appearing in more and more counties.

In many instances roe deer were the first to colonise, possibly for two reasons: firstly their numbers grow more quickly – roe does are fertile at the age of one and they frequently produce twins – and secondly they are satisfied with smaller woodlands. Colonisation by fallow deer, although much slower, more localised and in smaller numbers was also noticeable where larger woodlands gave them their required habitat. Migration by red deer in England was small scale and only very localised.

There was, however, significant post-war migration by muntjac deer from central England outwards, to the present situation where muntjac are widely dispersed throughout England. Again their rapid spread can be attributed to multiple births and having no annual breeding season, thus a doe can conceive more than once a year. Being small they remain unnoticed until there is a sizeable population of them in a locality.

Of the 'new deer' neither sika nor Chinese water deer have colonised much of the country, sika more so than the Chinese water deer, the latter requiring habitat conditions which allow for their selective feeding. Sika while spreading more than many realise, have limited their presence to areas of thick woodland, often purely conifers where they thrive; they are now controlled and contained by stalkers.

Over the last 60 or more years, the land-use industries have been encouraged by HM Government to make Britain more self-sufficient in agricultural products and timber. To satisfy the growing demand for both, the advances in mechanical and chemical technology of agriculture and silviculture has produced a state of over-production of agricultural products in the last twenty years. Similar concentration on forestry has resulted in large afforestation programmes throughout the British Isles.

Afforestation has had a greater direct impact on deer, their distribution and migration, than agricultural changes. It is a fact, however, that whilst little success has been found in chemical deterrents protecting crops from deer damage, the wide use of agrochemicals has resulted in deer abandoning feeding in the fields for a time after the application of certain chemicals.

The forestry industry has provided a deer-friendly habitat in the post-establishment phase of afforestation which lasts several years, probably 8-10, until the thicket stage in conifer growing is reached and a longer period in the infrequent broadleaf forest. The importance of these woodlands, large and small, is that they provide an attraction to deer both in terms of food and shelter. The larger complexes will attract not only roe deer, but also the larger species. Today, afforestation is being encouraged by the Government through a variety of agencies on an increasing scale as an alternative use of land to reduce agricultural over-production. The industrial call for hardwood, the wildlife lovers' call for more natural and more beautiful countryside as well as the requirement for leisure facilities, and an attempt at purification of polluted atmosphere all play their role. Today we are talking of several Community forests, from the London area, through the Midlands and on to the Caledonian Forest. These forests, if they materialise, will provide vast areas of deer-friendly habitat. To make these projects attractive to owners, a variety of grants and concessions are being made.

But the Government involvement in deer matters is not solely of recent years. Under pressure from sporting organisations deer protection was introduced first in Scotland then in England and Ireland in the 1950s and early '60s. Under Scottish legislation the Red Deer Commission (RDC) has been established as an official advisory body with limited powers to ensure control of red deer in Scotland, while the Nature Conservancy Council (NCC) has been given powers to licence specific deer control and other activities. The RDC, whilst doing very creditable work in establishing the size of desired populations of red deer on the hill has been powerless to positively influence the control of deer to reduce numbers, whilst the NCC has not had the expertise to professionally administer their licensing and other powers related to deer. The RDC's power intially related to red deer and more recently to sika. It does not include deer in the state forest in Scotland, where the Forestry Commission has sole responsibility, nor roe and fallow deer. Neither is there an official controlling body in England other than the somewhat ineffective NCC. As a result whilst we have some notion that the Scottish hill deer population is numerically too large by perhaps as much as 100%, we have no notion how many deer of all species 'hide' in the Scottish and English forests. However, we do know that roe deer, for instance, which were localised 30 years ago in England now live in just about every county, with no one responsible for systematic control.

This situation, in conjunction with inadequate education at higher levels in the management of deer, suggests that the planning of new woodlands, whether it be small farm woodland created under the Farm Woodland Scheme as alternative land-use, or large Community forests, may lack adequate know-how to ensure not only provision for deer, but perhaps more importantly to prevent unecessary and wasteful deer damage. Similarly, every time a new stretch of motorway is built, strips of woodland are being planted to add attraction to the appearance of the road, again attracting the deer; a clear illustration of how lack of knowledge of deer, and lack of wildlife related know-how brings deer into the immediate proximity of fast moving traffic and creates a hazard!

At the same time the desire for leisure has led many organisations to seek more access to land. The right to trek and watch wildlife on or off approved footpaths makes deer more timid, and the efforts to control more difficult, and even dangerous to the public. Not least are the protectionist, anti-blood sports activists irrationally protesting against the control of deer by sportsmen who do it as efficiently as is possible. The success of such protests risk the growth of the deer population becoming out of control, to the detriment of the habitat and the public.

1.3. British Cervidae

Introduction

WHILE there are six species of deer in Britain, only two of these are native: red and roe; all others have been introduced, some on purpose, others by accident.

There are many similarities between all deer species, not only the six British ones, but there are also some differences. These are better presented separately lest they get 'lost' among the other information.

Of the six British species, the males of five carry antlers, only the Chinese water deer is antlerless. Two species have prominent canine teeth, muntjac and Chinese water deer, and in the latter they are very long (5 cm).

Roe are unique in a number of ways. Their rut is at a different time to all the others, coming at the end of July. Their young are born in May/June. They have what is known as delayed implantation, also referred to as dormant gestation; the embryo does not start developing until early spring. They also shed their antlers earlier than the others, October to November, and have the new set clean by the end of May (young deer are later in cleaning than the old ones, as in all species). The other different one is muntjac; apart from having longish canine teeth it is unique in that it has no rutting seasons. A muntjac doe comes into season soon after her young have been born, which can be at any time of the year and can conceive immediately. That also means that the antler shedding cycle, which is geared to sexual activity, has no set time.

All other British deer have a rutting season from late September to mid November, dropping their young during June. There is always a possibility of a late rut, followed by late calving, but these incidents are uncommon.

In all deer dentition develops in a similar way but the time taken for the change from milk to permanent teeth varies – muntjac is said to take about 30 months, roe and Chinese water deer a year, the other three larger deer, about 24 months. Tooth wear and eruption is a method of roughly estimating deer age (see Chapter 2.2), but tooth sectioning is the only accurate method of deciding exact age.

Another difference between species is that some deer have a more distinct caudal patch than others; principally sika and roe, whilst the red, fallow, sika, muntjac, and Chinese water deer have distinct tails, usually on a light coloured 'target'.

Habitat

When the Caledonian Forest, the natural habitat of red deer in Scotland, was no longer, Scottish deer did not vanish; they persisted. Not for the first time in the history of nature did animals change their pattern of life to adapt themselves to the changing environment. No doubt in this transition many perished, unable to find enough food of sufficient quality and quantity in the new surroundings, which were devoid of trees and provided no more than grasses, herbs and heather, and no protective shelter or cover.

In this process of adaptive change Scottish hill deer developed a smaller skeletal structure including antlers. A smaller body meant less 'space to fill', perhaps a longer, more water and wind resistant winter coat, and a slower development towards maturity with a greater tolerance of bad weather. Other more intricate changes include resistance to conceiving at too young an age as an aid to survival. Perhaps one can also detect a change in the senses – a keener eye to detect movement at a greater distance than was necessary in a forest, and a keener sense of smell to back-up the distance spotting.

To my knowledge we have no records of antler sizes, body weights, fertility rates etc. of the pre- and post-Caledonian Forest era; records start probably in the late 19th century, hence we are unable to compare with any degree of certainty the 'old' with 'new' deer. In woodland deer versus hill deer however we have a clear indication of the differences which have occurred as the result of habitat change. The differences can be quantified in body sizes, woodland stags – 18-30 stone, hill stags 14-18 stone, which is a weight decrease of between 20% and 30%. Woodland hinds give birth at the age of two, certainly three years, hill hinds rarely at two, more likely at three or even four years.

An important characteristic of the old self-regenerating forest was that it was largely broadleaf, perhaps broadleaf with pine in Scotland, and as such, forests were attractive to deer and other wildlife. For years however, forests were being grown for human purposes, for war-making, industry and fuel. The early human impact on self-regenerated forest was small, for demand was small and felling selective; what was felled regrew from seed. As demands grew and artificially planted forests came into being so felling ceased to be selective and took the character of clear-fells with a large scale impact on wildlife. A new style of forestry industry was born, and with it the Forestry Commission as the official patron and policy maker was established.

The regime adopted by the Commission resulted in many thousands of acres of uniform conifer forest carpet covering large tracts of the country. For alleged production efficiency, fast growing timber for the building, mining and paper industries was the order of the day. Large areas were being planted simultaneously, with as few rides and tracks as possible. The notion was that simultaneous maturity would give the opportunity for clear-felling, followed by re-planting. To utilise the ground, area planting with the closest acceptable espacement measured in inches and not yards between the trees was practiced.

At the early post-planting stage, the new forest gave a haven to all manner of wildlife, providing food and cover. As the trees grew and the canopy closed, ground vegetation vanished for lack of light, the wildlife friendly habitat became hostile to all but a few rodents and selected birds. Only the margins on the boundaries provided some ground for food.

To popularise forestry successive governments were offering incentives by way of planting grants, tax relief etc., attractive to organisations and individuals with funds for investment.

From sometime in the mid 1960s, firstly for aesthetic reasons, then for ecological considerations, pressure was being exerted to change the appearance of the re-afforested countryside to give it variety. The accent was on re-introduction of broadleaved trees. Resistance to this pressure was not broken until the late 1970s, and not until the mid 1980s were grants for broadleaf planting introduced. At the same time a policy of wildlife friendly landscaping of new forests was introduced, including wide firebreaks, rides and roads, not only changing the aesthetic appearance of the forests but also creating an eye-catching habitat suited to woodland dwellers such as deer. From the deer management point of view, the landscaping with its woodland meadows and wide firebreaks offered facilities not only for observing deer but also for control culling, which under the old regime of dense forest was all but impossible.

Common Characteristics

There are some common characteristics of deer physiology and habit which must be understood if we intend to rationalise deer management.

Diet and Feeding Habits

Although deer are herbivores, we tend to subdivide them into grazers and browsers. Whether such a subdivision is justified is open to doubt because deer are selective in their choice of food, not exclusively one or the other. Their choice of food is related to the quantity and quality of food available to meet their energy requirements. While they are adaptable, the adaptability is not limitless. The controlling and regulating factors for deer are food and shelter, especially in harsh weather. When natural food is inadequate in quality and quantity, deaths occur – sometimes numerous and accelerated by the inadequacy of shelter in adverse weather conditions. Without human assistance in enhancing the quality and quantity of food available to deer, nature becomes the numerical controller, preserving the stronger and more resilient.

Being opportunistic feeders, deer accumulate energy during seasons of abundant food and store it in the form of body-fat and marrow, to be used up during times of food shortage. Furthermore, during seasonal shortages there is also a decrease in deer food searching activity calling therefore for less expenditure of energy. This is further emphasised by long resting periods in weather shelters which also saves energy. We can thus explain the ability of some deer e.g. roe, to build their antlers during comparative food shortages and an unregulated sex life as in the case with muntjac. Also worth mentioning here is the fact that we have an example of a self-regulating food intake system in Chinese water deer, which are capable of dropping their winter demand for food to some 30% of summer intake immediately following the first frost. To a greater or lesser degree this regulating instinct can be found in all deer and can have a far-reaching effect. The development of appetite at the first sign of an early spring which is often (in Britain) followed by spells of cold and 'non-growing' weather and therefore lack of food can have a big effect.

There are also records which show that deer select carefully. For instance there is the case of young trees in a plantation being devoured by deer, whereas in a similar plantation in the locality with the same tree and deer species, not a tree was being touched while deer concentrated on bramble, abundant in that location but not in the other.

Digestion

Deer are herbivores living on vegetable matter containing cellulose fibre. Their complex digestive system has adapted to take in large quantities of food, chew it, swallow, regurgitate and re-chew until it is adequately reduced to assimilate the digestible and reject the indigestible, cellulose being broken by rumen flora.

This process means that deer feed rapidly, eating large amounts in relation to their size, in feeding bouts. Between the bouts they rest and chew the cud. The length of the feeding bouts and chewing time differs between species. It changes depending on the type of food intake since some deer feed more selectively on vegetation of higher value taken in comparatively small quantities. There are also vast differences in food availability between, let us say, winter and late spring and food needed for antler building, lactation, post-rut, and other less active times. There are also differences of availability between hill and lowland, hill and woodland; and food availability linked to climate. In general terms one can assume that during the time of high feeding activity in March and April most deer need to feed every two hours, the length of feeding bouts depending on type of food.

Antlers

The antlers are also a common feature of all British deer other than Chinese water deer. The 'odd deer out' Chinese water deer grows no antler – his distinguishing feature being long (up to 7 or 8 cm) canine tushes.

Of the British deer only males grow antlers, a cervine characteristic. The difference between antlers and the horns of other ungulates is that antlers are normally grown and shed every year, a new set of antlers being grown as soon as the old ones are shed, whereas horns grow on from year to year becoming perhaps longer or thicker, or both, every year.

Deer antlers are the fastest growing structure of any animal, showing an enormous metabolic capability including assimilation and utilisation of a significant mix of minerals. The antlers of a deer can represent as much as 5% of body-weight (woodland red deer at 180 kg can carry 9 kg antlers), all grown in 4 months, or as little as 0.5% of the body-weight in small deer like muntjac.

Antlers grow from two bone base disks, known as pedicles, protruding from the frontal bone of the skull. The growth of pedicles is linked to the growth and development of testicles and the first antler grows normally when testes growth is complete (not necessarily meaning the animal is sexually mature). The development of the pedicle is complete by autumn in roe kids and develops as a small knob like a cap at the top, which is shed in late spring to grow the first proper antler (often referred to as 'head'). In other deer born in June and July, the pedicle is not fully formed until spring when the first antler in the form of a spike starts developing. In muntjac the antler development starts at the age of about five months, by which time the pedicle is fully developed. Antler growth, under normal conditions lasts about 104-107 days in muntjac, 120 days in sika and fallow deer, and 125 days in red deer.

During the time of annual growth antlers are richly supplied with blood, have a nervous system, and the tissue is covered with furry skin known as velvet. The antler is sensitive to touch, attracts flies and midges and being soft is easily damaged in contact with hard objects; such damage can result in deformation of the antler which lasts until it is shed. Damage to the pedicle however, causes a permanent deformation of the antler.

When the antler is fully developed and hardened, the flow of blood is cut off at the pedicle, the velvet dies off and is rubbed off against tree branches, bushes, heather and suchlike.

The first antler growth is no more than a knob or a spike on each pedicle, and each year a more complex formation grows, increasing in numbers of tines. There are however limitations: muntjac rarely grows even the brow tine, which is highly valued as a rarity, roe seldom grows more than three points aside with anything more than a six pointer head being unusual, sika rarely grows more than four points aside, usually in a formation similar to red deer. More than eight pointer heads happen rarely, when they do they might indicate hybridisation with red deer. Only fallow and red deer when adult, tend to grow more complex multi-tined heads of antlers, fallow usually with the typical palmation.

At an advanced age the complexity of antlers degenerates, the tines grow shorter and thicker gradually, some disappear completely; this phenomenon is referred to as 'going back'. (More detailed information about the antler development will be found under species headings).

Antlers and Sex Organs

There are certain aspects of deer physiology which have to be understood in order to throw into the right perspective a number of characteristics in the life of deer which affect management.

In all deer antler growth is directly associated with testicular function, hormone providing glands, and particularly with the build-up of the sex hormone testosterone. Hence abnormality or damage to the testes results usually in malformation of antlers. The case of hummel (antler-less male red deer) is unique in that although they are incapable of antler growth they are capable of reproduction.

Fig.1   ANTLER AND TESTES DEVELOPMENT CYCLE

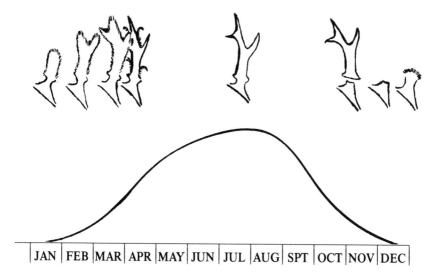

| JAN | FEB | MAR | APR | MAY | JUN | JUL | AUG | SPT | OCT | NOV | DEC |

There is, however, a linkage between antler growth and light cycles, and artificially created light cycles can create a different (more frequent or less

13

frequent) development of sex hormonal activity, thus changing the life cycle and therefore antler growing cycle. While light may have a programming role to play, the growth is regulated by the hormonal system through the pituitary gland which controls other gland functions including the testes which produce the sex hormone testosterone.

The antler is hard a few weeks before the rut, at the same time as the testes are reaching the peak of their yearly hormonal activity, except in muntjac.

Antler Growth and Deer Damage

When the antler is hard its surface is covered with small knobs (known as pearls), the grooves along which blood vessels ran form long 'ridges and gutters'; making the antler surface rough. When rubbing the rough surfaced antler against young trees, the tree bark is damaged – fraying takes place, a common form of damage in many woodlands. This happens twice a year – once when the velvet is dry and needs rubbing off and again before and during the rut. The older and stronger the animal the thicker a young tree he will use for fraying. It creates semi-permanent or even permanent damage to the tree; if fraying completely encircles the trunk the tree will die.

Displays of Power Pre–rut and as a Sign of Stress

The display, common among bird courting, has a physiological connotation. It is part of a reflex ritual show of strength, physical power and attractiveness of the individual. In this display male deer resort to the damaging activity of threshing – attacking young trees and bushes with the antlers and often breaking them. The size of the tree is relative to the size of the animal; a fully mature woodland stag can break a 15-20 cm diameter tree.

Similar attacks on trees also sometimes happen among deer as a sign of stress and frustration, for instance when too many find themselves fenced in too small an area of land. It could be stress brought about by hunger, or by inability to escape confinement or to join or round up the females during the rut, or indeed escape from a chasing master male. States of stress are sometimes also accompanied by bark stripping, an indication that it may be brought about by hunger or the lack of some mineral found in bark.

Having said that, we are not wholly certain what general purpose the antler is meant to serve. It is accepted that the primary purpose is not as an offensive weapon, although they can be used in defence, and sometimes in aggression especially during the rut. It is likely that the primary role is as an indication of power as an attraction for the opposite sex, like the display in some birds and other animals. It is probably also an identification mark, maybe even placing the animal in a certain place in the hierarchy of the herd.

Senses

All deer have highly developed senses to detect and evade predators and other enemies.

Hearing is probably the most acutely developed and the system is adapted to exclude background noises such as wind – this is achieved by the growth of hair inside the ear acting as a dampener. It seems that woodland deer rely on their sense of hearing more than hill deer.

The 'defensive' sense of smell is highly developed and more acute in woodland than hill deer. The sense of smell is intensified by a deer licking its nose, sometimes lifting its head and baring its teeth. Deer have a set of highly developed scent glands used for communication between the animals. Some scent glands are more developed in certain species than in others.

Eyesight in woodland deer is comparatively less developed than in hill deer. In general both have poor eyesight compared with some other animals, being able to distinguish probably no more than shapes and these only at reasonably close distances; they are, however, very sensitive to unusual and suspicious movement. Deer can distinguish some colours and have an acute ability to distinguish contrasts of colour.

Whether deer have a highly developed sense of taste is debatable. They can certainly distinguish between varieties of food they find and select the preferred ones with surprising precision; whether this is done by taste or smell is hard to tell, there being a link between the two anyway.

The sense of touch is clearly different from ours. Firstly we rely basically on our hands and fingers, extremities which deer do not possess. There is a fair amount of body contact between all animals, with a copious use of muzzle and tongue, especially between the mothers and their young and also in sex play between the two sexes.

The senses used as defence mechanisms become adapted to the environment and surroundings. Deer living near settlements and cultivation are more tolerant of humans but wary of human behaviour, such as attempts at concealment. Deer living near transport routes tolerate traffic to the extent of ignoring it and being killed or injured, but they are alerted by a car stopping and put to flight by car doors being opened, even quietly.

Feet and Tail

The legs of all deer are very slim but muscular, allowing them to jump significant heights. The feet of all have cloven hooves with dew claws at the rear. In normal walk the track shows a narrow gap between the two cleaves, at the canter and gallop the cleaves open up forwards and the dew claws leave a definite mark. In the gait, the feet of the male are slightly 'flatfooted' (open-toed), whereas the females are more or less parallel.

Part One: The Principles

All deer have a tail but in roe deer it is just about invisible, being no more than tufts of hair which are white in bucks and yellowish in does.

Body Build

Allowing for differences of size, general body shape and life span, the appearance of deer changes with age. These changes are shown below in both illustration and tabular form.

Fig.2   BODY BUILD RECOGNITION

Roe deer

Young buck (2-3 years)

Medium aged (4-6 years)

Old buck – 9 years or older

Red deer

3 years   Yearling   4-6 years

7-8 years

Very old   Old

Old hind   Calf   Weak hind

Some main recognition features are shown below:-

MALES	YOUNG	MATURE	OLD
Neck	thin	filling	thick
Head	erect	high	low
Belly	small	tight	drooping
Shoulder	covered	showing	protruding
Flanks	slim		hollow
Rump	angular		rounded
Gait	brisk		ponderous

FEMALES			
Neck	slim		thin
Ears	erect	stiff	flabby
Belly	slim	full	drooping
Flanks	slim	full	hollow
Milk glands	none	showing	baggy
Appearance	inquisitive	alert	alert

Dentition

Deer have two kinds of teeth: four pairs of incisors at the front of the lower jaw and three molars and three premolars on each side of the lower and upper jaw. In muntjac and Chinese water deer canines are always present and in this species they are as significant as antlers are in other deer. Vestiges of canines are normally present in red deer but rarely in roe.

Deer use the incisors by biting against the hard skin of the upper jaw. As they cannot cut through much of their feed, they tear it and here lies the difference between twigs bitten off by deer and by rodents, the latter being able to cut cleanly with upper and lower incisors (important in distinguishing damage).

The cheek teeth are the grinders and shredders of food and cud in preparation for ultimate digestion. They become worn down during the lifetime and in old deer are often the cause of death, because chewing and grinding of food becomes impossible.

The teeth develop in a uniform fashion in all species but the timing of this development differs and is related to the life span. Deer are born with incisors and three premolars, all of which are milk teeth. The first molars develop as permanent teeth: in muntjac they appear in about the fifth week, in roe in the third month, in red and other large deer in about the ninth month. Roe has all its permanent teeth by the time it is about 13 to 14 months, larger deer by about 24 months, in muntjac they are said to take 30 months but the sequence of growth is always the same, as is the history of wear.

Fig.3   DEVELOPMENT OF TEETH OF THE LOWER JAW

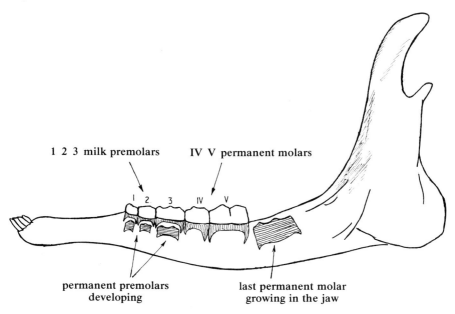

1 2 3 milk premolars   IV V permanent molars

permanent premolars
developing

last permanent molar
growing in the jaw

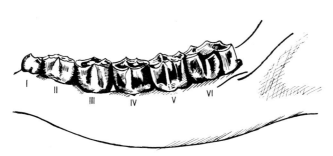

full set of permanent teeth
(Roe deer at 13 months, Red deer at 30 months)

Pelage

There are some common characteristics in the pelage of deer. In the first place the hair covering the pale skin surrounding the tail and perianal region is light coloured, sometimes almost white with darker, sometimes blackish surrounds. This hair erects as a warning sign to others, usually a sign of danger and fright. There are also obviously different hairs covering the scent glands. In different species they are different in colour and length but the hairy locations make the gland location stand out; in muntjac gland surrounds on its head are devoid of hair.

Red Deer

1. Distribution

Fig.4   RED DEER DISTRIBUTION MAP
                              Updated 1989

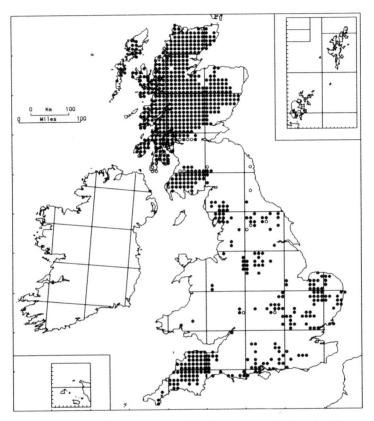

Copyright Biological Records Centre, I.T.E. Environmental Information Centre
Irish records are not available

2. Description

There are two varieties of red deer in Britain, woodland/lowland and hill. In zoological terms they cannot be regarded as two sub-species, because the differences of size, fertility and antler development are enforced only by habitat differences. A young red deer moved from the hill to a 'better living' soon loses its hill characteristics and develops woodland ones.

The most striking outward difference between hill and woodland red deer is the size of body and antlers. A hill hind stands about 90 cm (36 ins) at the shoulder and weighs between 65-90 kg (10-14 stone), a hill stag stands 105-125 cm (42-48 ins) at the shoulder and weighs about 95-115 kg (15-18 stone), a twenty stone stag is heavy. The woodland hind stands 105-125 cm at the shoulder (42-48 ins) and weighs 80-115 kg (13-18 stone), the stag will be 115-135 cm (45-54 ins) and 115-190 kg (18-30 stone), whilst the calves which in the hill variety may weigh 6-7½ kg (13-16 lbs) may reach 9-13 kg (20-30 lbs) in the woodlands.

In stags the different habitat is also reflected in the antlers. Hill stag antlers are comparatively short, thin and lightweight: 70-80 cm (27-32 ins) and 2 kg (5 lbs) in weight are fair averages, whereas 90-115 cm (35-45 ins) and 4½ kg (10 lbs) are the comparable woodland stag's equivalents.

In hinds the different habitat affects reproduction; a hind living in woodland may be capable of reproduction from her first rut, certainly from the second onwards, whereas her hill sister rarely conceives before the age of three and often not until four.

PLATE 1   RED DEER

(photo by P. Yates)

3. Habitat

Red deer are by nature forest dwellers and they need forest for their optimal development. In some parts of Britain (and elsewhere), notably in Scotland since the disappearance of the Caledonian Forest, red deer have been forced to live on the open hill and have adapted themselves to that environment. The price they have had to pay for living in a poorer habitat is the size of their body and antlers and a change in the behavioural pattern and feeding habits.

Red deer do not take well to large, dense coniferous forests as a permanent habitat but will use them as shelter. They will, however, thrive in large broadleaved forests.

4. Feeding Habits

They are adaptive and opportunistic feeders, feeding in bouts which last varying lengths of time depending on the quality and quantity of food available. Being ruminants, the structure of their stomach requires time to chew and regurgitate the cud before full digestion takes place; for this reason deer require resting/chewing periods between feeding bouts. These periods, spent lying down, usually take 2-2½ hours. On the hill deer feed moving into the wind, and rest/chew lying with or across the wind; having said that it is always important for them to be able to overlook danger areas which they need to keep in sight. In woodland deer the feeding bouts are of the same frequency but, because of better food availability, the feeding period is shorter. The orientation whilst feeding and resting in relation to the wind is perhaps of lesser importance.

Red deer raiding agriculture causes significant damage of a two-fold variety. On winter wheat or barley it is not what they consume that is damaging but what they trample down into mud. On roots, their tooth structure is not equipped to deal with turnips and beet; they uproot a plant, taking often no more than one bite from it, and leave it barely eaten, to rot. (See also Chapters 1.5 and 3.1).

5. Social Structure

Hind groups operate in a definable pecking order. They are under the dominating influence and guidance of the 'lead hind' which is usually an older animal. It is she who determines the feeding areas and leads the herd on the move. In situations of suspected danger it is the leading hind that is first to investigate, and signals to the rest. A stamp with a foot or a short barking grunt are the most usual signals. She also decides on the retreat to safety, if one is necessary. In a large group there may be a second hind guarding the rear of the group. The loss of the lead hind usually leads to the herd splitting into smaller groups. Any dispute within the herd is often decided upon by hinds rearing up on their hind legs and lashing at one another with the forelegs – this is referred to as 'boxing'. When smaller family groups join up into a herd the lead hinds fight for dominance by 'boxing' each other.

Hinds are territorial; they stay within their 'home range' which usually is determined by the calving area; hinds do not stray away from this area, and return to it and to their calving stand year after year. Having said this, the actual day-to-day location of the herd within the home range is determined by feeding, weather and shelter and often fine-tuned by infestations of flies and midges.

By early September on the hill and late August in the forests the older stags, now in hard clean antler and with full mane growth, 'break out' from the stag groups and start looking for hinds in anticipation of the opening of the rut. It is the older, heavier stags which are the first to reach the hard antler stage. They become 'travellers', seeking hinds and herding them together towards the traditional rutting stands. This tendency is triggered off by a combination of an increasing level of testosterone, linked to the length of the day/night cycle and influenced by the first hinds coming into season.

The rut is a time of dramatic change in stag behaviour. From a social group animal they now treat all other stags as rivals for possession of hinds. Stag herds split up and a movement of individual stags with their harems of hinds towards the traditional rutting stands is evident.

For the rut stags develop their characteristic and unique voice. The roars (challenges can be compared with anything from a prolonged bellow to a lion's roar) are mingled with grunt and cough-like calls, all of which start as soon as the older stags begin collecting their hinds in September. This happens earlier in the forest and later on the hill. The challenges last as long as the hinds are in season. Therefore, if a single hind comes on heat in December, stags start roaring.

During the rut stags fight for their hinds. Most of the combat, awe-inspiring in its speed and ferocity as it may be, lasts only a few minutes and rarely results in the death of contenders. There are usually head-on collisions between the contenders, with an enormous expenditure of energy, with clashing of antlers and straining of muscles from neck to hind legs in a pushing combat. In this duel, the larger heavier stag usually wins and chases the contender away. A day comes, however, when the master stag, spent by the energy of covering hinds and fighting contenders, is no longer capable of defending his hinds and is defeated, and a younger stag or stags take over. Flanking attacks do not often happen, but when they do they are usually deadly.

There is a large degree of correlation between a stag's age, body-weight, and antler size which gives the older stag an advantage in his attempt to collect and retain a good hind herd, serving them as they come into season. This advantage will also allow him to get to the best rutting stand with the best food in the vicinity. He is soon disadvantaged, however, by the large number of younger contenders which, in spite of losing energy in sparring, fighting and running away when chased and so losing some of their condition, have more stamina and staying power, being younger and more agile.

After the rut the 'run' stags return briefly to either the high ground or to their previously occupied areas of forest to feed and rest. On the hill they are forced down by snow and wind, and the better lower feeding grounds are already occupied by the hinds, so the stags feed either on 'second best' or move on to agricultural crops. The forest stags have less of a problem and usually fare better but even here both stags and hinds may resort to stripping the bark of trees, presumably in order to find otherwise insufficient bulk.

There are significant differences in family life between the hill and woodland herd. Large herds of as many as 100 hinds, certainly upwards of 50, and somewhat smaller herds of stags are not uncommon on the hill while herds of a dozen woodland red deer are normal, and two dozen would be large. This may be simply explained by the fact that woodlands offer better and more evenly distributed feeding – lesser concentration therefore in better feeding areas, and better protection – fewer pairs of eyes needed to detect danger. There is also a difference in the way the protective senses have developed. Smell is very acute under both hill and woodland conditions. Hearing is less important to the hill beast than it is to the woodland one, hence the hill red deer's sense of hearing is less. The eyesight is about equal, responding more to a detection of movement than acute definition.

During the summer and early autumn the hinds live in comparatively small family groups of a few mothers and calves and yearlings; the 'smallness' of the group differs between the hill and woodland. The main attention is directed towards feeding to build up stores of energy (fat) to help the animals survive the winter. This is especially important for calves. As the rut approaches the family groups are herded together by older stags who come into rut first, leading and herding the hinds to the traditional (or habitual) rutting stands. The timing of oestrus is determined by the hinds' condition, weight and age. A hind that has not been covered will come on heat several times in intervals of a few days; this may continue into November or even December, giving rise to a very late calving. Clearly, there is a need to cull out a late rutting hind at the first opportunity.

After the rut the hinds and stags separate and hinds with their families join in herds of increasing size. In the hills the hind herds seek the winter feeding grounds, which are usually lower, with better feeding. They occupy the best feeding grounds before the stags. The winter snows and weather may push the stags down to agricultural land where they maraud. There is a similar but less obvious movement in woodland. Even here however, in the areas of coniferous wood with poorer feeding, marauding on arable land is a frequent occurrence.

6. *Life cycle – Hinds, Calves, Stags*

A pregnant (or gravid) hind drops her calf in early to mid-June; the exact timing depends on the weather, habitat and the date of being successfully covered. A hind with calf is known as a 'milk hind' whereas one that has not calved is a 'yeld hind'; but if unable to produce young, she is 'barren'.

Close to calving time pregnant hinds assemble in nursery areas which on the hill are usually the lowest ground with better quality grasses and herbs, ideally with access to shelter from the sun and with water and wallows. Water for both drinking and cooling, wallows for cooling and protection against flies.

Prior to dropping the calf a hind will seek isolation from the rest of the herd, not distant, but apart from the others; at the same time she develops a unique call known as 'calving bellow' (the only time she can produce it). The timing of the actual birth will depend on her condition and the time of the previous year's rut. If she is in a good condition, and has wintered well she will be 'forward', come into oestrus earlier, be covered earlier and drop the calf earlier. The reverse is applicable to one in poor condition. It is also said that a male calf is carried a little longer, is somewhat heavier at birth and tends to be born later.

A newly born calf will be on its feet within an hour or so of its birth and will be helped by the hind to get up and start suckling. Once the calf has fed, the hind will eat the placenta, clean the calf and will leave it, sometimes for several hours, while she feeds herself. The calf is concealed in no more that high grass and herbage and remains motionless. Its spotted coat gives it excellent camouflage and being odourless it attracts no predators. It will remain motionless until the mother returns to it. For the first few weeks the spotted calf remains scentless and, to ensure this is so, the mother eats all the faeces and cleans it frequently. During this time the hind communicates with her calf by faint calls to which the calf instantly responds; these are not dissimilar to the call of a roe deer to its kid.

Over the following weeks, the calf feeds and is constantly in the immediate proximity of mother (unless resting) and this continues even after it is partially weaned. This close relationship continues and helps the calf to acquire the necessary habits and reflexes. With female calves it may continue throughout the life span, for the female calf will usually remain in the mother's herd, it will calve near the place where it was born, and will often immediately follow the mother within the herd, even when a year and more old being known as a 'follower'. Stag calves stay with their mothers certainly as yearlings (knobbers) and even later into the second or even third year (as prickets and staggies); after that they join the young stag herds.

Within the male deer group between the time of antler dropping and antlers reaching the full hard state, any dispute or even fight for amusement takes the form of boxing, not unlike the hinds 'boxing'. The beasts rear up on their rear legs and box with forelegs. The reason is that developing antlers are delicate and sensitive living tissues filled with blood and are easily damaged. During that time the warm living tissue tends to attract flies and midges, hence stags gravitate to higher fly-free ground in the hills, or a draughty and cool part of the forest.

7. Antler and Body Development

Soon after birth, the male calf starts growing small protrusions on the frontal bone of the skull known as pedicles. Antlers grow from these pedicles, a new set being grown every year. The first year antler-knob (hence 'knobber' stag) has grown as much as it is likely to do within 15 months of birth. Therefore, by September or October of the year following birth it will be hard and clean of velvet.

Velvet is a skin which covers the growing antler containing under it the blood vessels and nervous system of the soft developing bone. Once the antler has stopped growing the antler substance hardens, velvet and the blood vessels die, the nervous system is cut off and the velvet is rubbed off.

The knobs are shed the following late spring. There is a sequence in which antlers are shed. The first to shed are the old animals, and the last are the knobbers. Thus a knobber could still be bearing his small antlers in May and June, by which time the old stag has cast his antlers (as early as March, under some conditions even late February). Having immediately started to grow a new set of antlers by the time the knobber has cast the old one, the old stag has his antlers half grown. The second head starts growing as soon as the knobs are cast and develops usually into long beams. Under good conditions such as in the forest the second head may have tines, indeed under excellent conditions it could have three or four tines on each antler. From now on every year the antler is cast earlier, and completes its growth earlier. It should grow longer, thicker and bear more tines each year until it reaches a peak of development at about the time the beast reaches full maturity, which is probably at six or seven years of age. After that for a year or two the antlers remain more or less similar in size until with advancing age they start growing smaller, shorter, maybe thicker, and the tines start disappearing. An interesting characteristic is that from year to year antlers retain the same general shape.

Having cast early and started to grow new antlers early, the old stag will be in 'hard antler' early, probably by late August, and so will be ready for the rut early.

Basic Antler Shapes: Annual Growth and Going Back

Basically there are three general outline shapes of red deer antlers when looked at from the front. They can be described and are known as 'U', 'V' and 'Heart' shapes.

The 'U' is probably the most classic of all. In appearance the curve of the main beam is like the letter U, and if we disregard the tines of the crown, the general tendency is neither to converge nor diverge at the top. So, if the antlers grew indefinitely the tops would never meet.

In the 'V' shape the main beam is almost straight, showing a general tendency to 'open up' towards the top, so that with the growth of the antlers the spread becomes greater.

In the 'heart' shape the greatest inside spread falls somewhere between the crown and the trey tine. Above the points of the greatest inside spread the beams close in towards the top.

Fig.5   RED DEER – BASIC ANTLER SHAPES

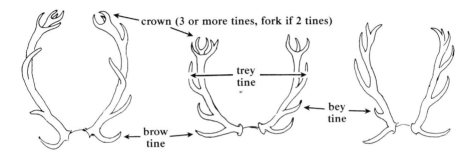

With the U and heart-shaped antlers, and sometimes with the V shape, there may be an additional guide to age in the shape of the brow tine.

In a well-formed stag, the brows start by being short compared with the bey or trey. As they grow longer so they show a tendency to curve upwards, and the angle between the line of the direction of the growth of the brow at the base, and the line connecting the base with the tip of the tine can be a basis for age judgement: the greater this angle the older the beast. This is not a rule but a guide, applying less to V shaped heads than to the others, mainly because in the former there is more of a tendency for the tines, like the beam, to grow with only slight curves. The exceptions to this are too frequent, however, to make it more than a sometimes useful hint.

The amount of annual growth is, of course, a great variable impossible to assess accurately, especially once a stag has passed the age of four or five years. It is on the growth of additional tines, therefore, and not on inches of antler length, that we must concentrate.

All deer, without exception, deteriorate with age. Not only does the venison get tough, but the body and antlers deteriorate in size and therefore in quality. Hill deer in wild conditions, exposed to all weathers, complete their development more slowly mainly because of poor quality food; their antlers are at the peak of development by the age of six or seven, their prime years being shorter with deterioration or 'going back', often starting by the age of nine. Woodland deer, living in a comparatively mild climate created by shelter, and with abundant food throughout the year, develop quickly so that by the age of six or seven they are in their prime, with deterioration starting three, maybe four, or even more years later. Here, as with so many of our considerations, we must look for many exceptions, such as park deer with no sign of going back at an old age and highland stags at the age of ten well set back; such phenomena are too frequent to permit us to make the ages more than a very general guide. Deterioration may be due not only to age but also to lack of adequate food during the antler-forming stage. This type of deterioration, misleading as it may be, will (or at least should) disappear if sufficient food is available in subsequent years and normal development in the following year should follow.

After a hard winter poor quality antlers may be frequent and the reason for this is obvious, but in individual cases it may also be that, owing to some upset of the digestive system in the winter months, a wound or illness, the beast has lost the ability to assimilate the required food for normal antler build-up, and has suffered a set-back as a result. With improving weather the animal's condition should improve, and given better health in the following winter, providing that the food is available, a normal head will develop.

At the peak of development the antlers will reach their maximum weight, length, number and length of tines, the best development of the crown and thickness of the lower and upper beam. The first sign of deterioration is normally the slight curving of the brow tine tips inwards or outwards, or a blunting of all tines. These are the first signs of going-back, followed by the shortening and blunting of tines of the crown or bay-tine. Usually, not more than one or two tines are affected per year, nor does the final going-back mean that all tines disappear completely, although it may be so in rare cases. The beam, having lost its length, will thicken, the thickness being greatest at the lower beam. The burrs, which in red deer are, in comparison to the size of the antler, much smaller than those of roe, will droop and form a ring-like extension of the antler, covering the pedicle. In some cases the deterioration of the crown is accompanied by webbing between the tine-ends. In these cases the top fork which remains after the disappearance of the crown will be of a heavy type.

There are several changes that take place in the structure and shape of red deer bodies. The definable changes are, tooth wear which changes with age, antler formation which also changes with age, and pelage which shows seasonal changes as well as some variations according to age. The shape of the body from being dainty as a calf becomes well filled and heavy with characteristics which allow us to distinguish the age group (pages 16 and 17).

8. Dentition

Red deer complete the change from milk teeth to permanent teeth by the age of 24-26 months. Both milk teeth and the permanent ones are subject to wear with age. The rate of wear is not constant, in some areas it is faster than in others and depends on deposits of abrasive grits on vegetation diet e.g. grass versus heather, furthermore the teeth of some animals are harder than others. It is tooth wear that gives us an opportunity to gauge the approximate ages of animals (see Chapter 2.2). But there comes a time when teeth are so worn down that the animal can no longer chew properly and its digestion cannot cope with the intake of unchewed food. It may die of starvation, even with its belly full.

9. Voice

Basically the red deer is a silent deer. However, the stags grunt, give slight barks as a sign of alertness and of course roar and grunt heavily and produce a cough-like call during the rut. The hind makes a gruffy bark when warning others of danger, or when unsure. In communication with the calf she makes a bleating call to which the calf responds with a bleat at a high pitch.

10. Pelage

The calf is born chestnut all over except the underbelly, tail and caudal patch and is spotted white. Sometime in July and August the calf loses the spots and starts growing a new fluffy coat which will be its first winter coat. That coat remains until about April, when it starts changing to summer red. In yearlings, by late August, the second summer coat starts changing to a winter one and so it continues; the change from summer to winter, and winter to summer coming later each year. It happens that these changes in an old milk hind are so late that, by the time she drops her calf, her coat is still moulting.

The summer coat varies in colour from grey and buff, through reddy brown to deep brown, always with a creamy underbelly and a grey rump with a small, short tail. The winter coat is grey to dirty brown.

Having said this, the weather plays a role in the coat change. In areas of cold weather the change to summer coat starts later than in mild weather locations; the shedding is also delayed by a particularly cold winter.

During growth of the winter coat, stags, from the age of two or three, start to develope a mane, which grows longer every year until advanced maturity is reached.

Overall the pattern of change is similar in both hill and forest red deer, but the hill deer's winter coat is greyer and marginally longer and thicker.

Fallow Deer

1. Distribution

Fallow deer have been kept in parks throughout the British Isles, and throughout that time there have been escapes and releases. Consequently, fallow deer are fairly evenly distributed from the southern counties of England with pockets spreading into Central Scotland.

Fig.6   FALLOW DEER DISTRIBUTION MAP
Updated 1990

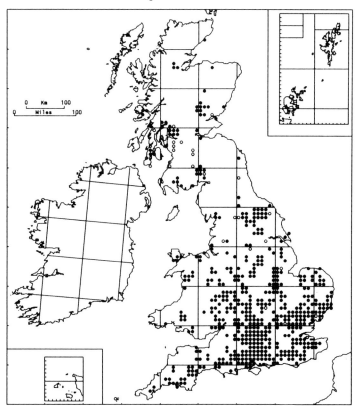

Copyright Biological Records Centre, I.T.E. Environmental Information Centre
Irish records are not available

2. Description

All European fallow deer are more or less of similar size, females standing at 80-90 cm (31-35 ins) at the shoulder, males being slightly taller at 90 cm (35 ins), and weighing 30-55 kg (66-121 lbs) and 60-100 kg (130-220 lbs) respectively. Apart from a variety of pelage colourations their distinctive characteristic is the adult buck's antlers which are usually palmated with a number of rear-pointing tines (spellers) and usually lacking the bey tine; females never carry antlers.

3. Habitat

Fallow deer are lowland woodland dwellers, having a preference for broadleaved and mixed woodlands beyond the thicket stage but with ample undergrowth cover. They tend to inhabit small and medium woodlands. Agriculture in proximity provides a proportion of their food.

4. Feeding Habits

Fallow are selective grazers and browsers. They browse heavily, especially on newly swelling and bursting buds and young shoots; it is this activity that gives rise to the creation of a 'browse-line' which is the level of the lower branch growth of trees which are browsed clear as high as the animals can reach. The feeding habit is centred upon grazing on grasses, herbs and fruits, not excluding cultivated fields especially winter cereals, hence they are often found in the fields surrounding woodlands during early mornings and evenings. With rumination pauses, every feeding bout lasts up to 2½ hours. In summer they may take up residence in pre-harvest corn fields.

5. Social Structure

Like red deer fallow live in herds. Adult bucks live apart from does for most of the year. Does, with calves and yearlings of both sexes recognise a defined 'pecking order' not unlike that in red deer hind herds, precedence being given to the leading doe. Bucks join the does during the rut, wherever they may be. The buck dominating a herd is very intolerant of other bucks and remains in the rutting stand until wholly spent. This is the main territoriality they show. Territories are marked by pawing and scraping the ground and threshing young saplings and bushes with their antlers. There appears to be no indication of the need to herd the does (like stags have to herd their hinds) but there is some chivvying by bucks walking around the herds. Bucks develop a groaning call during the rut, which they deliver with head held high but horizontally and tail curved.

Yearling bucks leave the does in the autumn after their first birthday and join young buck groups; they remain in these groups until they are 'allowed' to join the adult bucks at the age of about four.

Bucks and does live in separate herds much of the time and this can lead to distinct buck or doe woodlands, with bucks moving to the doe woodland for the rut.

6. Life cycle – Does, Fawns, Bucks

The doe drops her fawn between early June and early July, following a gestation of 220 days (approximately). The fawn is up and feeding (initially with mother's help) within a short time, certainly within two hours. The herds of females break up to allow births to take place in solitude. When not in mother's company, the fawn usually lies down motionless (and odourless) to avoid detection. Whether male or female it will stay with the mother for at least a year. The herds start to reassemble again after the fawns have been dropped, this time often with male company in preparation for the rut which takes place from September to late October.

After the rut, the young pricket males start gravitating towards the male groups which form herds and break away from the females. Older bucks often live singly or in old-buck-groups.

Herds are often large, female herds larger than male ones. Large herds however are likely to be collections of smaller groups feeding together in preferential places rather than permanent herds; careful observation will reveal that on returning to cover they break up into smaller herds.

PLATE 2   FALLOW DEER

(photo by P. Yates)

7. Antler and Body Formation

The young male fawns having grown their pedicles under the skin until about early February, do not develop any knob–like antler formation. In its place the fallow deer, now a yearling, grows a tuft of long hair before the first antler starts its growth.

The first antler is formed as a single spiked beam, and is velvet-covered until about the end of August, when the velvet is cleaned off. The velvet-cleaning time is slightly ahead of the older bucks, and this pattern remains, the older the buck the later (albeit by a matter of days) the velvet is cleaned off.

The first head (in the second year of life) should be the length of the ears, thick from the base upwards and thinning only in the last inch. Shedding time for the first head is between mid-April and mid-May after the older animals have shed theirs. Cases have been known of the first head being more than single-spiked, where either the brow has already started forming, or a slight flattening, a promise of palmation occurs on the very top of the antler. These cases are however rare.

The second head begins to develop within days of the first being shed, to be cleared of velvet before mid-September. This is the first head where good parentage and feeding may tell. A good buck at this age (the third year of life), should carry antlers consisting of the brow, possibly trey and a start of the palmation, most likely developed as a flattening of the top of the beam. In rare cases very well developed heads have a small palmation, probably spoon-shaped, even with markings of the spellers in the shape of an 'undulated trailing' edge of the palmation. On average a second head should be double the length of the ears, 12 ins (30 cm) high second heads being quite common.

Shedding of the second head takes place about mid-April, when the third head starts its growth. This head will normally be cleaned of velvet by early September.

The third head must have the brow and trey well developed and both these tines should be about two inches (5 cm) long at least. The palmation which was marked on the second head is now developed further, sometimes taking a triangular shape. Along its back edge there should be a number of rounded-off 'fingers'. These are the future spellers of the full palmation. Two of these tines should be more marked than the others, the spur (the lowest back tine of the palm) and the top-fore tine of the palmation. Both should be longer than the rest of the budding spellers, which are often no more than undulations with depressions and possibly a few (two or three) deeper divisions cutting into the palmation and running towards the base of the palm. These divisions at this age are quite common and should gradually fill in with the years.

The third head is shed about mid-April and the fourth head starts its development which will take until mid-September.

This head differs quite considerably from the previous one. The beam has thickened by now to support a fully formed palm with several spellers between the spur and top-fore tine. The latter should be pointed and slightly curved, the spur up or downwards and the top-fore forwards.

The fourth (fifth year of life) and older heads are only an advance on the third in the elongation of the tines of the palm and a growing of the head all round, and this process will continue for two or three years. The main advancement will probably be seen in the thickness of the beam, and the thickness and length of the brow and trey. The culmination of development of the head comes normally after the seventh or eighth head, after which going back may start. Bey tines do not usually grow.

There are locations where, possibly due to inherited characteristics or nutrition deficiency, palmations do not develop.

8. Dentition

The full set of permanent teeth is in position by about the 24th month of life.

9. Voice

During the rut, the buck's call is a repetitive coughing snort, rhythmically produced with a rising intonation. When spotting danger he is inclined to grunt. The doe grunts or coughs as a warning to others; she calls the kid by a bleating call, which is responded to by the kid by a similar but slightly higher bleat.

10. Pelage

Among the fallow deer in Britain we have several colour variants. Throughout the world there are said to be 14, in Britain we can account for fewer. The most usual is the common coloured variety – chestnut with prominent cream or white spots. In winter the coat becomes darker and the spots just about vanish. The rump is white, edged with black, and there is a black spinal line ending at the tail.

The next most usual colour variation is menil, which is like the above but the spots are retained in winter and the general colouring tends to be paler. The rump and underside are white but *not* edged with black.

Black or melanistic fallow deer are dark chocolate or almost black, without a white rump. The spots are visible at certain light angles and only at close quarters. Winter colouring tends to become grey in tone.

'White' fallow deer are usually a creamy colour, and are mostly found in parks or are recent park releases. Perhaps their pelage gives them no camouflage and they are more vulnerable.

In black and white fallow fawns the spots are barely visible, in others they are large in relation to body size; white fallow fawns start life with a ginger or sandy coloured coat.

Sika Deer

1. Distribution

Fig.7   SIKA DEER DISTRIBUTION MAP
                       Updated 1987

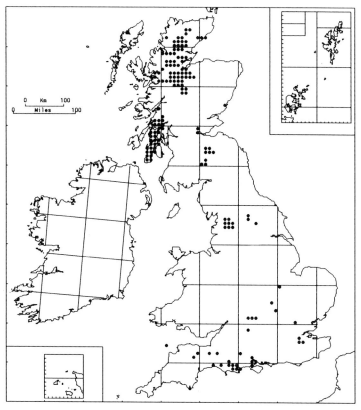

Copyright Biological Records Centre, I.T.E. Environmental Information Centre
Irish records are not available

2. Description

Japanese sikas stand a little smaller than red deer. They are about 80-90 cm
(31-35 ins) at the shoulder weighing about 40-50 kg (88-110 lbs); mature
males up to 65 kg (145 lbs). While similar to red in general appearance,
apart from colour, the stag does not grow multi-tined antlers, five points
aside is an unusually good head. Due to hybridisation with red deer, in
some areas the hybrids produce antlers with more tines. Hybridisation
has also led to colour variations.

PLATE 3   SIKA DEER

(photo by P. Yates)

3. Habitat

Sika have a preference for acid soil terrain to which they gravitate, especially in winter. Pine forests, Sitka spruce, larch with boggy ground and heather, all suit them. In summer they move to better, richer vegetation, venturing into cultivated land surrounding the woodlands. Sika have not taken to the open hill in Scotland and maintain their presence only in the neighbourhood of woodlands, hence hybridisation takes place within woodland rather than on the hill.

4. Feeding Habits

Sika are probably as selective as fallow deer, feeding heavily on grasses, broadleaf buds and twigs, heather, fruits and fungi. But they manage in thick conifers with rough grazing. They are fond of water-bank growth and are keen on hazel, which they are prone to chew and strip, in preference to other bark.

5. Social Structure

The behaviour of sika seems to differ between locations but in general terms it is similar to that of red deer. There is sex segregation in that hinds and young calves keep together. The stags, hinds or mixed herds are small, not unlike the woodland red deer. Stag calves leave their mothers in the spring of their first year and join the stags, certainly before the rut. Notwithstanding this, stags do associate with hinds outside the rut, and often in winter. Stags appear to be more timid and secretive than hinds.

Prior to the rut, which takes place during October-November, stags mark their territory, and although they tolerate other stags within their group, they will fight fiercely for possession of their hinds. During the rut much of their energy is spent threshing vegetation including young trees. At that time they can be dangerous, especially when wounded.

6. Life cycle – Hinds, Calves, Stags

The sika calving rate is high, higher than red deer by a good margin; probably 60% calving from all adult hinds. The rut is in October, spreading into November, late rutting occurs but no more often than in red deer.

7. Antler and Body Development

The general pattern and stages of yearly development of sika in body and antlers is similar to that of red deer. The basic difference is in the number of tines of the fully developed antlers. The likelihood of a head developing ten points or more, except in red deer/sika hybrids is small.

There are significant variations in the antler formation of hybrids, but there is no rule which can be applied to this.

Fig.8   SIKA DEER ANTLER DEVELOPMENT

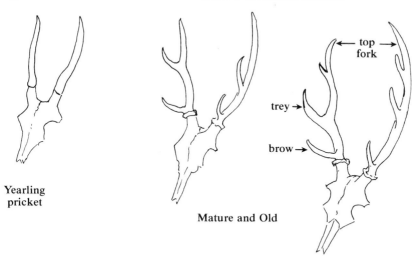

Yearling
pricket

Mature and Old

top
fork

trey →

brow →

8. Dentition

The growth of permanent teeth is completed by the second birthday.

9. Voice

The call of an alarmed stag is unmistakable, a short sharp whistling scream which ends with a grunt and more often than not is repeated after some seconds. The rutting call is a shrill whistle, first rising in tone, then declining to end with a grunt. There are long bouts of silence between the calls. Warning calls to rutting competitors are like a man 'blowing a raspberry' and the winter call is a squeak. The hind calls the calf by short screaming whistles; a similar call is made as a sign of alert. A hind on heat develops a special bleat, which is not very loud. The calf bleats like a fallow kid, and is not dissimilar to roe.

10. Pelage

The general colouring is dark brown with a tinge of buff, usually with yellowish spots, but the spots are not as striking as in fallow deer. Normally there is a line of pale spots along each side of the dark dorsal line which ends at the tail, which is otherwise white with a white conspicuous rump patch. There are white hairs covering the metatarsal glands on the hind legs. Stags are usually darker than hinds but not always.

The winter coat is darker brown, graduating to black, with a grey-brown belly in stags and grey in hinds; there are no visible spots. The head appears lighter coloured throughout the year. On the forehead above the eyes there is a lighter eyebrow chevron.

The calves are lighter in colour and more distinctly spotted.

Roe Deer

1. Distribution

Fig.9   ROE DEER DISTRIBUTION MAP
Updated 1990

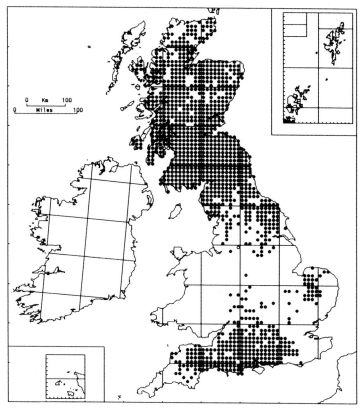

Copyright Biological Records Centre, I.T.E. Environmental Information Centre
Irish records are not available

2. Description

Roe is the most common British deer, distributed throughout the British Isles. They are highly adaptable to habitat.

The animals are 60-75 cm (24-30 ins) tall at the shoulder, bucks being slightly taller than does. They weigh between 17 and 25 kg (37-55 lbs), bucks in good areas reaching 22-30 kg (48-66 lbs). Does are always lighter. Neither sex has a visible tail and there is a patch of white hair at the rump, which can be erected when the animal is alarmed and is more pronounced in winter than in summer. In both sexes there is a small white patch by the muzzle reminiscent of a white moustache. Antlers in does are rare, and bucks' antlers vary in size, being typically 15-25 cm (6-10 ins) long with three tines aside, although more tines have been recorded.

PLATE 4   ROE DEER

(photo by Ray Hobbs)

3. Habitat

Roe deer are basically woodland dwellers, preferring broadleaf to conifer, but colonising young conifer plantations. They are usually found at woodland margins and adjoining fields. There are recordings, however, of roe changing their habitat from woodland to fields or moorland. In these instances they tend to form into small (in terms of roe deer) herds of two or even three dozen, finding cover in bracken, heather, hedgerows and rarely if ever returning to their natural woodland habitat. This rare phenomenon should not be confused with several family groups feeding together in fields of particularly tasty vegetation such as clover, especially at its first yearly flowering. Like fallow, they will return to their habitual woodland in separate family groups.

4. Feeding Habits

Roe are very selective grazers and browsers. They will take grasses, herbs and fruits, as well as fungi and spring heathers; they are keen on tree buds, leaves and young twigs as well as the bark of some trees, and occasionally stripping takes place.

In spring they will feed in the fields on winter cereals in the early morning and evening and also well into the night. They rarely feed outside cover during the day, except in winter.

5. Social Structure

Roe deer keep generally to their family units based on the doe and her young. The doe finds a buck at the opening of the rut. Bucks being territorial, remain within their territory for most of the year but defend it only from antler hardening in about April, until after the rut in August. During that time they mark and re-mark the territory and do not tolerate other bucks. Does have no territory and move freely over the bucks' territories. In spring and again in winter bucks can be seen with the does. Although kids normally live with their mothers, they are abandoned during the period the doe is involved in the rut. The kids call their mothers by bleating, to which the doe responds, usually returning to the kid. The calls and the doe's reaction often attracts the buck, and is 'exploited' by stalkers who may imitate the calls to bring out the buck to a shot.

In some parts roe deer do appear to form larger groupings. Opinions differ as to whether these are congregations of several families feeding in favoured localities or 'herds' of roe deer. Young bucks of one and two years old move often in small groups and can be found in their 'milk-bars'. A buck which after that time has not acquired his own territory, usually moves away to a different locality.

6. Life cycle - Does, Kids, Bucks

The rut takes place from late July to early August and is often affected by the weather. Hot stormy weather tends to accelerate it. On good hot days the height of the rut takes place in late mid-morning and early afternoon. After a dormant gestation overwinter, young are born in May. Twins are common, triplets do happen, but rarely do all three survive.

Within a few weeks of its birth, the male fawn starts growing pedicles which are fully formed by late autumn. A small cap-like knob of antler bone grows from the pedicle in winter and is shed in late spring, probably

Fig.10   ROE DEER – FIRST ANTLER DEVELOPMENT

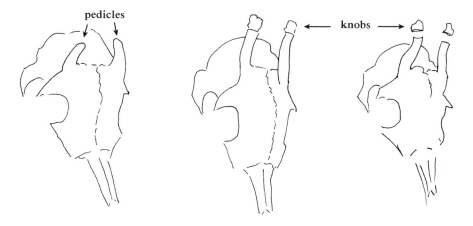

by late April, when the first antler proper, usually a spike, grows to be completed and cleaned by late rut in late July. Full six-pointer heads are usually grown in the third head; more than six-pointer heads are rare.

7. Antler and Body Development

As with red deer there are three basic forms of roe deer antlers. The 'U' or 'lyre' form, also known as the cup, in which the antler is curved low down and the beams, looked at from the front, grow more or less parallel to one another, increasing the inside spread very slowly towards the top or not increasing it at all above the bottom curve. The 'V' form is known as 'straight', as there is almost no curve in the beam, and from the burr upwards the inside span increases as the top is reached. The 'Heart' shape, in which the antlers first curve slightly inwards then outwards all the way, the greatest inside span being normally below the top fork.

Of these three basic forms the 'V' shape is least popular, and the 'U' and 'Heart' shapes are considered to be better trophies.

Fig.11   ROE DEER – BASIC ANTLER SHAPES

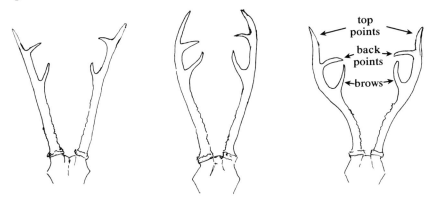

Inherited characteristics are more obvious in the roe deer than in red. The roe may reproduce a fault over two or even three generations, only the fourth generation showing a decline of the fault. In the same way as red deer, a buck, provided that development has not been disturbed by hunger, illness or wounds, will reproduce a head from year to year.

Annual antler development is slightly easier to describe than with red deer. Normally the well developed first head is between one-third and one-half its eventual fully-grown size, the second head reaches up to three quarters of its full size, and the third should be over 85 per cent fully grown.

From the fourth head on the only changes will be the gradual thickening of antlers from year to year, and thickening and widening of the burrs. A buck which has matured well in the fourth head should maintain his good characteristics for two to four years before the antlers start deteriorating (going back). The first sign of going back is drooping of the burrs. This takes place first on the outer side of the burr and spreads towards the front and between the antlers, the back being last to droop.

The antler, once it has started going back, loses length and the tines from year to year 'withdraw' slowly. It is not uncommon to find a buck which, having developed into a good length six-pointer by the age of four, by the age of ten has become a tineless spiker. Beams may be long or short but are usually thick. The brow tines are usually the first to disappear, followed by the back tine of the fork, which sometimes shows signs of webbing inside the fork.

The tines, before they disappear, often become blunt and rounded, with a dull surface and without polished white ends.

The body development follows the pattern of most deer.

8. Dentition

A full set of permanent teeth is grown by the 12th–14th month. Canine teeth are rare and when grown are very small.

9. Voice

Both buck and doe bark, not unlike a dog. The buck's bark is sharper, ending abruptly. The older the buck the deeper the bark. A doe's bark is shriller and the ending slightly drawn out. The barking may continue as the beast runs from danger.

The doe calls her kid with a 'pee-you' bleat sometimes sounding like 'peep-peep'; the kid answers with a bleat. Does on heat looking for a buck produce a piping squeal, whilst during the rut and being chased they produce a panting, gasping noise.

10. Pelage

In summer the colour is a rich reddy–brown on the flanks with a lighter belly. The muzzle is dark brown to black with light grey or white patches on each side. The ears are large with long white hair inside and are black edged. The rump is large, oval in shape and buff coloured. There is no visible tail. The coat moults in April to June with the young animals changing first, and again in October-November when the coat becomes grey-brown with visibly longer hair. The caudal disk is very white in winter pelage with a long white anal tush in does.

In some parts of the country roe deer have an under-chin white gorget patch. There are richer brown varieties allegedly in roe deer from the Continent. There are rare albinos, and black individuals have been recorded.

Kids are richly spotted with white becoming uniformly reddy-brown within six weeks.

Muntjac

1. Distribution

Fig.12

MUNTJAC DISTRIBUTION MAP
Updated 1990

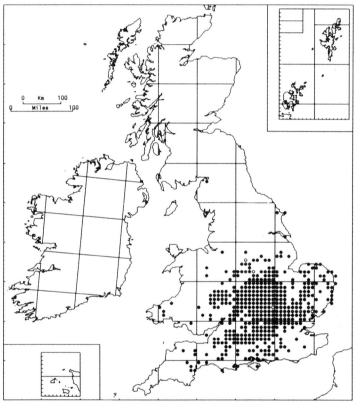

Copyright Biological Records Centre, I.T.E. Environmental Information Centre
Irish records are not available

2. Description

The muntjac stands at about 55 to 65 cm (21½-25½ ins) at the shoulder and weighs 11-16 kg (24-35 lbs), with characteristically small antlers on very long pedicles which are coloured black, start at the eye socket and are emphasised by the face colouration. In movement, its rump is higher than the shoulder. When alarmed the tail stands erect showing a white underside. Like Chinese water deer it grows canine tusks but no longer than 2-5 cm (1-2 ins).

3. Habitat

Almost entirely woodland dwellers; needing good cover and a supply of good nutritious feed. They like the thick cover of brambles and ivy, on which they feed.

PLATE 5   MUNTJAC

(photo by P. Yates)

4. Feeding Habits

Because their stomachs are less complex than most other deer, muntjac are highly selective, eating small amounts of highly nutritious materials. They feed predominantly on young leaves, shoots of trees and shrubs, as well as seasonal fruits and fungi. Herein lies the risk of serious damage; feeding near the ground, in thick cover muntjac can create an equivalent of the fallow and red deer 'browse line' but at a height difficult to spot. They will browse on young shoots of trees and other vegetation within their reach and be in competition not only with human cultivation interests but also with game and other wildlife.

5. Social Structure

Muntjac are secretive, living singly on the whole except for the weeks when females are accompanied by their fawns. Fawns are weaned at the age of about seven weeks by which time they become independent of their mothers who come on heat soon after.[2] The bucks are with the does usually only during the rut, but mixed pairs are not uncommon. It is the female who is territorial.

6. Life cycle - Does, Fawns, Bucks

Unlike other deer muntjac have no breeding season, hence it is difficult to establish when they start breeding. It is most likely that the female becomes fertile before her first birthday and probably between the age of six to nine months; bucks are fertile throughout the year. Twins are not uncommon.[3]

---

[2] Chapman, Norma, *Deer* (Whittet Books, 1991).
[3] Putman, Dr. Rory, *The Natural History of Deer* (C. Helm 1988).

7. Antler and Body Development

The usual antler form is a short main beam over 10 cm (4 ins) long, and rarely developing even one tine. As muntjac are fertile before the age of one they have the capacity to develop their first hard antlers by that age. Antlers are probably cast from May to July and second and later heads are cleaned from August to October.

Fig.13 MUNTJAC – ANTLER GROWTH FROM PEDICLES

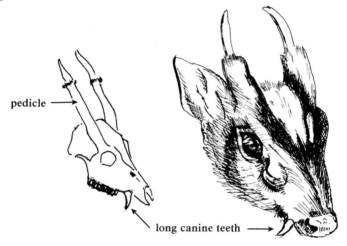

pedicle

long canine teeth

8. Dentition

Muntjac always have canine teeth which sometimes grow to 5 cm (2 ins) and which are always sharp. Surprisingly, their permanent teeth are not fully formed until the age of some 23 to 30 months.

9. Voice

Both sexes bark. Barking is repeated at intervals and can last for a long time. These are the calls of fright, excitement or from does on heat. Does and kids squeak to each other especially if separated. A frightened kid also bleats at a high pitch. There is also an unaccounted for clicking call as well as a loud, piercing distress call.

10. Pelage

The male summer coat is bay with orange tinges. It is more grey-brown in females, the tail is white underneath. The legs are darker sometimes tending towards dark browny black. The summer pelage is in place by May and the winter coat by November. It is uniformly dark grey-brown but the tail remains unchanged in colour. There is a well marked stripe along the pedicle and a dark brown patch on the crown of the head in females.

Fawns are dark brown with lighter coloured spots and a strip of chestnut along the back; this changes to adult colouring within six weeks.

Chinese Water Deer (CWD)

1. Distribution

Fig.14 CHINESE WATER DEER DISTRIBUTION MAP
Updated 1988

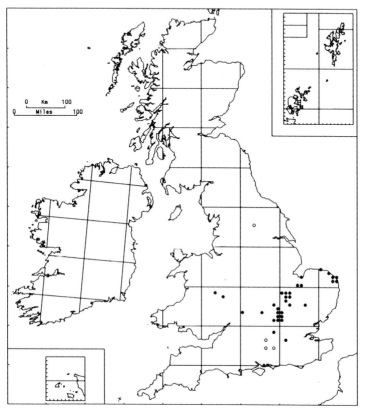

Copyright Biological Records Centre, I.T.E. Environmental Information Centre
Irish records are not available.

2. Description

Chinese water deer are about 50 cm (20 ins) high at the shoulder, males being slightly taller than does and they weigh between 8 and 15 kg (17-33 lbs) (males 11-15 kg, females 8-10 kg). Their notable characteristics are rounded ears full of fluffy long white hair, a lack of antlers in both sexes, and canine tusks growing up to 7.5 cm (3 ins) long.

3. Habitat

Habitat is probably the greatest 'holder' of Chinese water deer. They need woodland, preferably marshy woodland; woodland margins with good quality grasses and cultivated fields nearby. Being selective feeders they are attracted by the right habitat.

PLATE 6   CHINESE WATER DEER

(photo by J. Willett FRGS, FZS)

4. Feeding Habits

Selective and opportunistic feeders, they have the same characteristics and similar structure of stomach as muntjac; living, however, in more open country and fields. Chinese water deer are also very selective, relying largely on young grasses; they are especially fond of kale.

5. Social Structure

Probably because of their rarity not much is known about their social structure. They are secretive animals living singly or in pairs, the young developing quickly and leaving their mothers when about a year old. They live close to their feeding areas.

6. Life cycle – Does, Fawns, Bucks

Chinese water deer develop very rapidly to the degree where they can give birth to young by the time they are one. Fawns are born in May and June and by the rut in December they are sexually active. Twins and triplets are common with larger litters having been recorded.[2]

7. Antler and Body Development

There are no antlers in either sex.

8. Dentition

The full set of permanent teeth is thought to be complete by the time the animal is 11-12 months old.

The long canine teeth are the distinguishing characteristic of this deer. They are a defensive weapon of some importance, and are also used in digging for roots.

9. Voice

Occasional fights between bucks are accompanied by a clicking noise, probably produced by a rapid contact between the canine teeth and the teeth of the lower jaw. The alarm call is a harsh bark. The exchanges between the doe and her fawn are roe-like squeaks and bleatings.

10. Pelage

The general colouring is bright chestnut with black spots. The head and ears are buff with white surrounds to the nose and eyes. They have a white chin and inside ears. There is a very small tail but no rump patch. The winter coat is duller and uniformly yellowish grey with a slightly paler rump.

1.4. Deer in Conflict

F OR AS long as deer provided food, and venison was a staple diet, man and deer were not in conflict. The 'value' of a carcass of venison in relation to income was enormous. The thrill of poaching deer, for many years a forbidden quarry within the Royal Forests under Forest Law was, for many, even more valuable.

In Britain, with the exception of Scotland, wild deer in the open range have vanished – presumably having been wiped out. They were reintroduced, however, either by releases to the wild or escapes from parks, mainly during the 19th century.

Throughout the twentieth century industrial need for timber had to be satisfied as the constant and large-scale reliance on imported timber became strategically insupportable. To produce timber modern practice required the planting of fast growing conifers. The implementation of large tree plantations encouraged and attracted deer, but forestry policy was weighted against deer and they were either killed or fenced out.

The day came however when deer, uncontrolled by predators which had been exterminated by humans, proliferated and became pests. We have seen how deer multiply and how they tend to colonise newly afforested areas so it is not surprising that, as they spread, the number of suffering landholders increased and the rate at which complaints were being recorded rose.

The first to complain were farmers whose crops were being raided by deer, quickly followed by foresters when the modern forest practice of large-scale planting, which was the successor to wild, self-regenerating forest, became general practice. Forest establishment was a costly enterprise and as deer moved into newly planted areas of forest and had their fill of seedlings, plants and young trees, complaints multiplied. Defences against deer damage became necessary and the practices used ranged from fencing to killing and using all manner of deterrents.

Deer came into conflict with the master-race.

The conflict, 'the aggro', that deer seem to have created over the years was, so to speak, not of the deer's doing. We have used deer for venison and for sport, and we have abused them, because having denied them Nature's control mechanisms, we have failed to control them, often in selfish fear that we might not have sufficient stags or bucks for sport or not enough venison for a lucrative export trade.

Even to this day many refuse to accept the concept that deer must be controlled and that, at an appropriately low density, they can be managed as a source of good yearly revenue possibly with a value not much below that of timber, as will be shown later. This should be an important consideration in the forestry industry where most of the return on investment comes when trees mature, probably several dozen years after establishment. Many a forester, in whose veins flows the residue of the 'kill the deer pest' syndrome, shudders when faced with compound discounting being used to prove the value of deer in the same way as is done to show the value of forestry.

To understand the way to resolve the conflict to our benefit we need to analyse deer damage, its cause and effect, and practical economic methods of damage prevention and control.

Deer Damage

Is it reasonable to hope for a happy and economically viable symbiosis between forestry and deer, where the latter can be regarded as a profitable crop? If so, how can it be achieved? These are the questions which need to be answered as fully and clearly as is possible in relation to both old and new forests.

We cannot blame the forester for being hostile to deer when he sees areas of newly planted or growing trees damaged by them. Because the roots of this justifiable hostility lie in damage by deer, it must be better understood. Deer are recent, large scale colonisers of woodlands and forests; the damage they create is not fully understood even by the 'experts' and certainly not by the traditional foresters. Within the limits of this understanding we shall start by examining the problem, taking each type of damage and discussing its cause. Later in this chapter we will consider damage prevention (and tree survival after damage in Chapter 3.1) and also seek to find one of the answers – searching for the optimum level of deer density as a damage prevention measure.

Browsing

The main damage caused by deer while feeding is by browsing, mainly on young shoots and branches, buds and leaves of trees. Most harm is done when deer feed on the leading shoots of young plants and seedlings. These shoots are vulnerable for as long as they are within the deer's reach; their attraction is their palatability. Deer will browse throughout the year, but principally when other ground growth is dormant, therefore winter and early spring are the times of worst damage. Once other food becomes plentiful the deer tend to turn more of their attention to young grasses and herbs, and later berries. The browsed twigs look either chewed or broken because deer either chew at them with their lower and upper molars, or tear with the front incisors against the upper gum; hares, rabbits, squirrels and mice, cut the twigs with their upper and lower front teeth.

Browsing on sideshoots, while perhaps not desirable, is less damaging to the trees' future development. Granted it causes some retardation and gives rise to prolific side development at the cost of upward growth, but it is not always a killer.

All species of deer are guilty of browsing and indeed in the case of heavily populated mature woodland or parkland a browse line is created below which all growth on the adult trees has been browsed. Because the most damaging effect is from the browse on leading shoots, protection is needed until these shoots reach 140-150 cm for roe deer, 170-180 cm for fallow and sika, and 180-200 cm for red deer, whilst the muntjac damage is low, below 50 cm (see also muntjac feeding habits, page 45).

Browsing on side shoots is mentioned in this chapter as a means of preventing damage, for the prolific side development gives deer ample browsing on some trees, and limits browsing on the leading shoots of others. However, not all species of trees are equally vulnerable and it is often noticeable in mixed forests that some species fall victim while others remain untouched, or at least are damaged to a lesser degree (see Annex 1 to Chapter 2.6).

Often in young tree plantations, when the trees are vulnerable, those responsible for maintenance spend considerable time and effort weeding all the ground vegetation between the young trees either manually or by the application of herbicides, to ensure that unwanted ground vegetation does not compete with the young trees for light, water and nutrients. Weeding is also intended to discourage rodents and other pests from the plantations.

Such extensive and thorough weeding is, however, usually a mixed blessing. For the development of young trees it is accepted as being important so that the saplings establish themselves and grow as quickly as possible thereby passing out of the expensive maintenance stage. In some parts of Britain climbing and twisting weeds like clematis and honey-suckle tend to retard if not stifle growth. But the complete removal of ground growth between the young trees, having deprived the 'pests', deer included, of their naturally grown food, directs their attention to the succulent young trees, their tender shoots and in winter the bark or even roots – there is little alternative food to be had! Of course deer, being larger than the others, get all the blame.

Increasingly, therefore, herbicide weeding is practised only immediately around young trees.

Grazing in the woodland is not a damaging activity.

Grazing on Agricultural Land

We have devoted a lot of space so far to the damage in woodlands, which is not surprising because primarily deer are woodland animals. But they do not just damage woodlands, they also cause damage outside the woods.

Because we are concerned with cultivation we must consider damage to agriculture. The most common field damage is by deer grazing, especially on winter cereals, which is in some respects not lasting as is explained later. There is lasting damage to root crops, especially by red deer to sugar beet, and corn fields by lying-out in summer. The effects are more widely discussed in Chapter 3.1.

There is, however, other damage, forgotten by many, and more often than not, totally disregarded. That is damage to wild, natural vegetation. Probably the most important example of this is damage to hill heather in the Scottish Uplands by grazing deer and sheep.

There are areas of high deer population where heather is flowering less and less each year, because deer and sheep are grazing off the flower bearing young shoots, stopping self-seeding and self-regeneration. It is almost as if there were an opinion abroad that as the Almighty gave the hill heather He will look after it and deer and sheep will not kill it. It might have been so if man had not upset the balance of Nature by removing most of the predators and used much of the deer range for his own purposes.

Fraying and Threshing

Damage brought about by fraying and threshing is not connected with the feeding needs of deer. In its natural recurring form it is a fulfilment of certain physiological needs, normally confined to two periods of the year. Firstly when the animals clean the velvet from their newly grown antlers – in roe deer this is in March, April and sometimes early May – in red, fallow and sika deer possibly starting in late July with the main activity in August and September, sometimes extending to early October. Deer select for this purpose young supple trees, bushes and other growth offering resistance compatible with their own strength and preferably a rough and hard surface which helps to rub off the velvet from the now hard antlers. The damage to the bark and core of the tree is not from the velvet itself but from the antlers' hard rough surface. Roe deer at the same time mark their territory by leaving behind the scent from the gland located at the base of the antlers.

The second bout of fraying and threshing precedes the rut (July – roe deer, September-October sometimes stretching into November for the larger deer). The purpose of this may be twofold: it is a reassertion of territorial boundaries, particularly characteristic of roe deer and to a degree fallow deer. It is also sometimes used by other woodland deer to mark their rutting stands, and as a display of power and strength before or during the rut, be it to attract the attention of the females or to deter contenders from intrusion. In the larger deer species it follows very soon after antler cleaning.

There is another possible cause of fraying and downright destructive threshing: stress and frustration, which can be brought about by a number of factors. The only natural cause is the challenge to the territorial or herd master by younger contenders. The greater the challenge the greater the risk; the stronger the challenged beast the thicker the tree he can attack; trees 3 m high and 8 cm thick can be broken by stags. It might mean, therefore, that the greater the deer density, the greater the chance of challenge, and the greater the risk of threshing.

Fig.15   **RED DEER**
'Downright destructive threshing'

Frustration and stress can also be brought about by unnatural factors such as being fenced in too small an enclosure, being denied access to suitable or habitual rutting stands, being denied access to females, having the habitual routine excessively disturbed and suffering protracted and frequent intrusion by humans without a means of escape.

Take just the first example: fencing. If a significant number of deer are fenced-in within a forest block which for instance lacks food, or in some other way provides an unsuitable habitat, threshing may start with the fence in an attempt to break it and then spread to the trees. The same may happen if the number of deer has increased significantly within the fenced forest block, and at the same time the habitat has deteriorated (e.g. after canopy closure the supply of food has decreased). Threshing can break out, either gradually or as a spontaneous outburst, possibly triggered by some additional motive. The inclusion of deer leaps as a means of escape invariably helps.

Stripping

In the first place we need to understand that stripping is a habit fairly common among red deer but far less common in fallow and in roe deer, other than perhaps during very hard or snowy winters. Stripping is often attributed to stress. There is little doubt, however, that deer strip bark from certain trees to satisfy feeding needs at times of specific food shortage – the question remains whether they are seeking bulk roughage, water, minerals, vitamins or sugar or whether there are some other constituents of bark which they require. The analysis of bark suggests that there is some important nourishment value in it, even when compared with mid-quality grasses. Surprisingly, for instance, stripping sometimes occurs near deer feeding stations; does this suggest that stripping is occasioned by boredom, or is in search of additional nutrients which are lacking in the food available.

It is believed that stripping tends to be started by the females (especially of larger species of deer, roe rarely resort to it) and the males take it up later. It also seems that once started, it is difficult to arrest. Various experiments attempting to identify the causes suggest that the provision of roughage, salt or carbohydrates tends to reduce its incidence.

The lasting effects of such damage are uncertain but it does seem that summer damage has a more significant lasting effect than damage which is inflicted when the tree is dormant and the sap is not rising under the bark. It also stands to reason that in winter there is less risk of infestation by fungi and bacteria which can cause heart rot and the deterioration of timber value. It must be emphasised that it is not only deer that strip the bark – so do rabbits, hares and squirrels. Deer stripping bark do so with an upward movement of the exposed lower incisors and they then tear the strips off. Other bark eaters cut the bark, usually horizontally, with the cutting surfaces of the lower and upper incisors working against each other.

Not all species of trees are vulnerable. Deer seem to have a preference for oak, spruce, Douglas fir, pine, poplar, willow and ash but there are some variations both geographically and climatically.

There is no doubt that when bark is stripped around the entire circumference of a tree it is bound to die. But otherwise, the tree shows a large degree of resilience and a capacity to recover, healing and regrowing the bark. The timber however remains scarred and that affects its economic value (see also Chapter 3.1).

Damage Prevention

Over the years, the agricultural industry has developed a complex armoury of chemical antidotes for the damaging activities of weeds and insects upon crops, and fertilisers, which supported by modern technology are so effective in enhancing production that they give rise to over-production. Ironically, this technological intensification has not taken place without some adverse consequences; the use of some agro-chemicals has brought about changes to much of the bird life through the disappearance of many invertebrates – and we all miss the colourful additions to the countryside of moths and butterflies. Myxomatosis was introduced as a means of rabbit control which has decimated the rabbit population, and so influenced the decreasing predator population. The rabbits developed immunity together with a change in their life style but not their fertility. Agricultural fertilisers are used in forestry, as are some herbicides, but the costly attempts to produce an effective chemical deer deterrent have so far not succeeded as the results are not weather proof.

Woodland Pests

Any discussion of woodland damage by animals must acknowledge that deer are not the only culprits and it is even debatable whether deer damage is always the most significant one. All too often deer, because they are large and can be seen, are blamed for the damage done by others, from sheep and cattle which can stray and play havoc in woodlands, especially in young plantations, to indigenous pests.

Deer as pests can be controlled by culling or by fencing, both widely used and equally effective methods. Other culprits, like rabbits, hares, squirrels, voles and mice who, cumulatively, can create very significant damage, especially in winter, often escape unnoticed, and evade or survive control. Deer are blamed because most people who should know, in fact, do not know how to differentiate between deer damage and damage by other culprits.

In recent years, in locations where damage by animals other than deer has been identified, experiments have been made with the re-introduction of those birds of prey which feed primarily on small mammals and only occasionally on birds and bird chicks. This approach has been used even in areas of significant game bird population. It has been found to be a success, and environmentally it is constructive by restoring some of the vanished bird population, but it is slow in development. By keeping the rodent population in check it is supportive to forestry. Furthermore, after the initial costs, it is a self-maintaining process and thus not expensive. Many gamekeepers who have not tried, probably shudder at the very idea, but it was in fact tree minded keeper/foresters who developed the concept.

Area Protection

Area protection can be viewed either as a means of containing deer within an area thus preventing their escape and intrusion where they are not wanted, or protecting an area by not allowing deer into it. To a degree it is a matter of scale and the economics of the undertaking as well as the species of deer presenting the danger. The methods described below attempt to provide at least the basic answers.

Small Woodlands

To protect small woodlands, the usual approach is to prevent deer from entering at least for the first few years after the establishment of the trees and to this end fencing is effective. The type of fencing used, the quality of material and standard of its maintenance will not only determine the duration of its effectiveness but will also depend on the species of deer which present the hazard. Indeed in recent years some forests have adopted a policy of 'short term protection' – erecting conventional or electric fencing to last for the few years of particular vulnerability i.e. from establishment to about mid thicket stage. This approach saves significant maintenance expense and can be applied equally to small woodland plantations or larger plantations within older woodland complexes.

Roe Deer

Sometimes, to prevent roe deer entering, rabbit fencing is erected. It is of small mesh thin wire, often topped with a strand or two of wire. Firstly, unless the fence is at least 1.5 m high, it will not keep roe deer out; they will jump it and jump between the topping wires. Secondly they will break the fence with either their antlers or by running into it and straining the mesh. Once broken, the mesh becomes weak and the holes are quickly and easily enlarged. All too often it is not appreciated how strong roe deer are and how flexible and small in 'cross section' are their bodies. Kids are quite tiny and will get through an opening of a few centimetres; after such penetration the mother persistently attempts to get in to join the kid. Sometimes the mesh is too large and allows roe deer to squeeze through; the same applies to fencing comprising just strands of wire, even if these are close together. The guideline to follow is that if a rabbit can get through so will a kid, and if a hare can get through so will adult roe. Muntjac and Chinese water deer, being smaller, get through even more easily. It is all important that even if a short-term fence is erected, it is formed from materials which are durable enough to survive the required length of time.

Electric fences are an effective deterrent against roe deer provided that they have a stand-off wire. Roe deer habitually follow fences before jumping them and if they can be kept sufficiently far away from the main fence to discourage them jumping, they will not attempt it. Needless to say, if the current fails, or is shorted (perhaps by long, wet ground growth) or if the electrified wire is covered with snow, the fence ceases to be effective and penetration will take place. An electrified stand-off wire makes fence jumping difficult and is an added protection.

Individual tree shelters of the polythene sleeve variety, although not designed as a deer protection measure, are becoming increasingly popular. They tend to be used on broadleaves more than conifers. Ideally they need to be staked to make them and the plants inside them wind-resistant. They also have to be high enough to prevent deer reaching the leading shoot and browsing on it. Polythene seems to be attractive, however, to some rodents who tend to damage the base of the sleeve. Furthermore, in some areas, it has been found that the shelters cause the plant inside to 'cook'; therefore they should be staked, leaving a gap at the bottom to allow air flow inside. Polythene shelters act like a greenhouse and the plant develops faster than it would otherwise; the penalty may be that it is more delicate for the first year or two after the shelter disintegrates or is removed.

Red and other Large Deer

Protection against red and other large deer is usually achieved by fencing. The fence needs to be at least 1.8 m high, whether it is tensile steel wire or electric (preferably with a stand-off strand). The durability of protection again depends on both day-to-day and long term maintenance (see Chapter 2.6).

Polythene tree shelters are not generally considered suitable for large areas because of their cost nor are they suitable for the larger deer species. Nevertheless their use is increasing, especially to protect certain selected trees (selected by species or by location in relation to damage).

Visual and Acoustic Deterrents

Visual deterrents such as lines of coloured flags or reflecting mirrors, and acoustic deterrents such as hooters and bleepers or other sound scarers are not suitable as long term large area protectors. They tend to be used to prevent encroachment into roadways, gardens or even through gaps in a fence while it is being repaired. The effectiveness of these measures wanes as the animals become accustomed to them so acoustic deterrents are more effective if the sound effect is irregular or ideally is 'on demand' (photo-electric cells and infra-red switching have been tried). Visual deterrents are more effective when they have movement, like a beam of light from a moving vehicle being reflected in a mirror and sweeping round as the car approaches or twisting foil hanging in the breeze.

Large Areas

Traditionally it has been considered that effective protection of large areas is only practical when fencing with high tensile steel, usually of a welded mesh variety or even electrified wire is used. Some very encouraging results have been obtained recently from well laid out and well maintained electric fences used to contain both large and small species of deer. They have the added advantage of fast erection and relocation.

Forest Lay-out and Design

The modern approach is to design the forest (Chapter 2.6) recognising the presence of deer as inevitable and capitalising on their presence as an asset. This approach, provided it is backed by careful control of deer density within the limits of forest capacity, also allows for dispensing with traditional fencing which not only saves costs but also improves the general appearance of the countryside.

Fencing

Whether the area in question is large or small those involved in decision making regarding fencing are facing a dilemma; it is not only whether to fence, and where and what to fence but primarily what fencing to use. The Forestry Commission, both as land owner and as private forestry controlling body, as well as the Red Deer Commission recommend the types of fencing to be used (Annex 2 to Chapter 2.6). The cost of fencing with the recommended materials is high. It is further confused by various sources quoting prices for fencing which are for unsuitable materials for deer fences. Unsuspecting landowners read of fences competitively low priced per hectare as being acceptable for 'all animals' and do not ask whether the fence is to be for stock, rabbits, or red deer. Here is where the basic misunderstanding appears to be. There are some, who for economic, aesthetic or other considerations, decide not to fence at all and accept the risks of deer damage. There are others who accept the risk in the knowledge that sound management will minimise damage.

It is because fencing is a significant cost that it needs to be carefully planned and in any such plan the level of risk is the first consideration. There are not many regions of Britain where deer are not in evidence; perhaps not locally resident but within a migration distance of several miles. Once an environment is created which is attractive to them, deer, especially roe, tend to colonise it. Colonisation starts with one or two deer only, but soon others will follow and in a few years there will be too many for comfort.

It may be tempting to solve the problem by creating a 'hostile environment' by the cultivation of only those timber crops which do not attract deer. However, even among the trees which are not attractive to deer, there will be an enticing ground cover, with the trees providing the required shelter. So a hostile environment is not easy to create, especially in woodlands, orchards, shrubberies, tree nurseries or plantations. Furthermore, a tree which is not browsed may well be used for fraying. It is also difficult to predict whether deer will not 'take a liking' to some tree species which hitherto or elsewhere, has been avoided. (Annex 1 to Chapter 2.6).

Having taken the decision to fence, the next question is when and where to fence and which fencing to use. Suffice it to say that fencing should be erected before cultivation, as a part of the planning and preparation stage.

Fencing needs to be planned. In addition to its general layout in relation to the cultivation area, consideration must be taken of the habits and movements of the local deer. Such planning calls for a knowledge of the locality, as well as the ability to forecast what the deer will do when the fences have been erected. It also needs foresight as to what the colonising deer might do if they became established in the forest in spite of fencing. Fence planning, therefore, has to be a joint effort between a deer expert and his agri- or silvi-culture counterpart who has the knowledge of the overall main crop plan – in both the long and short-term. Together they must consider the relationship between deer and the various aspects of crop growing and age-related vulnerability of species, planting technology, time scales and future possible crop rotations.

Only through carefully developed strategies can a sensible plan be developed, which includes the selection of the most economical and yet most effective fencing for the job. Having said all this, however, it is likely that deer, sooner or later, will find a way into and out of a fenced area. It only needs a snow drift in a suitable place, a gate left open, a section damaged, or a stream flood carrying flotsam to create a break in an otherwise impenetrable fence, and deer will be let in. Once in, they rarely if ever get out. (Forest design and fencing are discussed at length in Chapter 2.6).

Lastly protection measures other than fencing should be at least reviewed, for some of them have produced very positive results.

Chemical Deterrents

There are conflicting views on the use of chemical deterrents in large areas of woodland. The major drawback to their use is that most of them do not stand up to the British climate. Also, many are labour-intensive, requiring either brush-on or spray application. Large scale spraying, aerial or vehicular, while possible, is practical only in plantations and not woodlands from the thicket stage onwards, although aerial spraying has been successfully used in insecticide application. Many deterrents are thick substances and therefore their spraying is difficult if not impossible. In order to reduce costs the formation of a deterrent barrier of a few rows of sprayed trees surrounding a vulnerable area, or application to selected trees within the woodland has been tried. The varying results obtained often stem from such influences as gaps being left in the barriers created or animals being left inside the barrier, trapped and unable to escape. Generally, however, the effectiveness of chemical deterrents lasts only for as long as the deterrent itself is active – days or weeks, or perhaps at best a few months depending on the weather.

Food and Other Additives

In cases of damage associated with feeding, provision of additional food or food additives tends to decrease the level of damage. However, the feeding of deer within the forest, or on high and remote hill locations, is often not practicable although the provision of certain additives may be.

Research in Poland by E. Szukiel[4] suggests methods which have been successfully applied in defence against stripping (see also A.J. de Nahlik,[5]) as follows:

1. Silage made of bark strips and twigs mixed with vegetation attractive to deer (cabbage leaves or beet leaves) in the proportion 1:1:1; also pine bark with cabbage leaves in the proportion 7:3. The latter takes longer to be accepted because the bark needs more chewing, but at the same time this is a better preventive. Silage is taken by deer more eagerly in frosty than in mild weather.

2. Bark. As an alternative, logs of felled trees up to 60 years old can be provided. These logs are placed on supports 30-50 cm above the ground. Deer will strip up to 80% of the bark so provided (up to 100% if the logs are occasionally rolled). Deer stripping a pine seven to eight years old can obtain only between 0.05 and 0.2 kg of bark, depending on the variety of pine, whereas a felled tree of 30 cm diameter at base and 20 m long provides between 5 and 20 kg of bark. Such a quantity of bark is equivalent to between 650 and 1300 trees of the age of 8-16 years being stripped.

It has been suggested that one of the causes of bark stripping may be the need for roughage or possibly for certain minerals and carbohydrates which bark contains. Where this is the case manufactured licks containing urea (to break down cellulose in the food intake) with trace elements and carbohydrates may reduce the damage level. The same type of

---

[4] Szukiel, E., *Defence against stripping* Acta Theriologica (IBL Warsaw, 1981) Vol.26.

[5] de Nahlik, A.J., *Wild Deer* (Ashford Press, 1987) 2nd Edition.

block is of help on the hill where deer are forced to consume quantities of old woody heather and are in consequence undernourished. (Not a question of damage on the whole unless the heather is being over-grazed).

The advantage of the above methods is that they can be used in those parts of the forest where stripping damage is prevalent or where trees are at a vulnerable stage.

Large Scale Feeding

Feeding deer on a large scale is widely practised in Continental forests, but is rare in the United Kingdom except in deer parks. As a management practice it is applied where the forests hold a higher density of deer than the habitat can naturally and economically support; if deer were not fed, the damage would increase. In some forests which do not present an adequately supportive habitat attempts are made to retain the deer and even improve their quality, by the practice of large scale feeding.

There is little doubt that deer well fed 'artificially' with a well balanced range of supplements do not create excessive damage through large scale browsing. This is not the place to discuss the ethics of feeding as a management practice.

Small scale feeding is, of course, often practiced, even on the Scottish hills, using urea and other mineral blocks to help deer break down the otherwise indigestible fibres of old heather. Some concern for deer at the end of the winter and the early, lean period of the spring also gives rise to additional feeding in many locations.

Bark Scarring

The scarring of conifer bark with a sharp, fork-like tool has been used for decades in many Continental countries as a deterrent. The practice induces an outflow of resin from the broken bark. It has gone out of use because it is a highly labour-intensive operation.

Recently, with the outbreaks of stripping in some German spruce forests (reports refer to the Sitka variety but it is more likely to have been Norway spruce, the error being a linguistic one) bark scarring has been re-introduced as being one of the more effective and simple to use deterrents. Selective applications and mechanical labour saving devices are being investigated and if the requirement for this type of implement continues, it stands to reason that mechanically or electrically powered scarring implements will be manufactured.

In all this the most effective damage preventive is careful and well planned control of deer numbers in the area. Deer density is the subject of the next chapter.

Damage Prevention – Myth or Opportunity

We have to accept that deer damage is inevitable. The cause, as has been described, is the fulfilment of physiological needs and these cannot be changed. The fact that deer do damage makes us, or should make us even more alive to the need for their control. It is fortuitous that the requirements of deer control, maintaining the population at a low level, is not only essential to achieving damage reduction (not eradication which is usually unattainable) but also leads to improvement of quality.

It stands to reason that only a finite supply of food is available to deer in a given area, especially within the limits of damage tolerance. There is therefore an inverse ratio relationship between the quantity of food *per capita* of deer and the deer density, therefore a better opportunity to build up the body, health and antlers, which are all important considerations in the economic management of deer, at low levels of deer density.

Therefore, deer damage *per se* cannot be stopped completely. Even within the fenced areas, sooner or later, deer will break-in and colonise. If we suffer damage at least we can turn our efforts to minimising it by keeping deer numbers in check. This serves the additional purpose of making our deer better quality and thus increasing their value as a usable and manageable asset.

Total damage prevention in other than very small areas is a myth; planned damage minimisation, however, is an opportunity which not only decreases the losses to the primary crop but also improves the return from the secondary crop – the deer.

1.5. *Deer Density and Capacity*

I F WE are concerned at any time about deer damage our attention should be addressed to the density and distribution of deer, for high deer density and high localised concentrations spell disaster. And yet deer density as a concept is not fully understood and very much under-explored and under-researched in this country, and the concept of capacity even less so.

The consideration of density of deer is important in relation to damage prevention – it must be very clearly understood, therefore, by those responsible for deer management as well as those responsible for the well-being of the forest.

Many people talk about deer density loosely, linking no more than the number of deer in relation to the defined unit of area. Others just talk of numbers of deer over the area of the deer range, estate or whatever. All too rarely it is recognised that, if we wish to control deer damage through controlling density, what we must know is the density which can be accepted or tolerated. In reality, what is the acceptable capacity?

Because the concepts are not clearly understood as important aspects of management I quote below their definitions (my own definitions):

1. Density – is simply a figure which relates the number of deer in a given area to a measure of that area expressed in acres or hectares. One usually talks of the number of hectares per head of deer, or number of deer per 100 ha (1 km sq).
2. Capacity – is the number of deer expressed either in an absolute sense (capacity of estate X is 2000 head of red deer) or the density figure, which, in the eyes of the management can be sustained on a given section of ground, within the acceptable level of damage tolerance. Hence the 'capacity' of a tree plantation is very low (damage risk is high therefore tolerance is low), whereas the capacity of a thicket is by comparison high (damage risk is lower and tolerance higher). Capacity is also expressed in number of deer per 1 or 100 ha.

There are several ways in which one can look at capacity, depending on who is looking. But whoever he or she is, they must consider capacity not as an abstract, but an acknowledgment that it establishes specific parameters as related to the deer species and the characteristics of the particular area.

The first consideration must be that of the level of damage and overt utilisation of the habitat which can be accepted by the owners. Here, consideration of deer species and the vulnerability of vegetation to damage are the underlying issues. Owners with different objectives will have different criteria for acceptability or tolerance of damage:-

1. Pure nature conservationists may take capacity as that density of deer, on the given land, at which the deer (and other animals) can survive above starvation level, on food naturally found, without excessively damaging the vegetation beyond the level of natural recovery.
2. Deer managers, concerned with conservation and control may take capacity as being the density of deer at the level where deer can live on the natural or supplemented food (depending on the owner's policy) and allow for at least a retention and ideally an improvement in deer quality in terms of venison yield, calving rate, antler development and general health. In cultivated areas some consideration must be taken of the damage suffered by the crops.
3. Forestry (or farm) managers may take capacity as that density at which the ultimate timber crop (or farm crop) lost to deer damage is in value at least compensated by the income from deer; in the forests, over the period of forest maturity.
4. Sporting managers may think in terms of the optimum sustainable yield – with a density which will enhance the breeding of the highest attainable deer quality.

In these definitions there is implied or explicit reference to deer numbers, size of area and vegetation which represents the deer feeding platform. The variables, apart from species of deer, are the vegetation (which can be wild or cultivated) and its resilience to deer (and other animals), grazing and browsing (or the owners' tolerance of damage).

Taking it all into account we can therefore talk of capacity of land area expressed in numbers of deer over the area (density) at which deer meet the owners' criteria in 1, 2, 3 or 4 above, i.e. at the level of damage (or use of vegetation) which is tolerated by the owners in their policy.

To put density considerations into context we need to compare how the deer densities in Britain (where they are known) compare with broad yardsticks elsewhere:

Scottish Hill : 3 red deer per 100 acres (40 ha)= 1 per 33 acres (13 ha) is considered to be low; high can be three times the number of deer thus close to 1 deer to 10 acres!
The Scottish Landowners' Federation recommended figure is 1 : 30 acres and RDC suggest 1 : 20.

Woodland : We have no British data for the density which various woodlands carry. Density however must be well below that on the hill for the sake of damage prevention. As an example of woodland deer densities couched in very basic terms we can take Hungary where state forest administration controls all deer management policies, densities are targetted as below:

1 red deer to 76 ha (1.3 to 100 ha)
1 fallow deer to 49 ha (2 to 100 ha)
1 roe deer to 20 ha (5 to 100 ha)
(1 hectare = 2.47 acres)

So how does hill density of 1 red deer to 33 acres (13.4 ha) of the Scottish hill compare? A crowd!

The Hungarian densities provide a useful scale for a comparison of densities of the three main deer species.

In the world of forestry we talk of trees and the ground vegetation as being cumulatively the feeding platform for deer. In this we recognise that the feeding potential of the forest changes dramatically between the time of establishment and felling. The tolerated capacity has to be related and adjusted according to the vulnerability of trees to damage at different structural stages (tree species/age structure) as the main criteria. Some European studies include variables such as availability of water and mineral composition of the soil. This is because deer may seek water and minerals which they do not find naturally by grazing and browsing on the available vegetation.

An approach covering this ground has been developed by Professor Mottl[6] who allocates feeding coefficients to the forests with trees of different species at different ages. The coefficients are expressed on a simple scale of 1 – 10 from low to high feeding potential (more about Mottl's work is in the Annex to this Chapter).

Fig.16   FEEDING POTENTIAL OF TREES
(based on Mottl)

AGE OF FOREST							
Species	1–5	6–10	11–20	21–40	41–60	61–80	80+
Pine & Larch	6–9	½–3	0	1–3	3½–6	6–8	F
Fir & Cypress	5–7½	5–7½	0	0	0	3–6	F
Oak & Birch	7½–10	7½–10	4½–6½	6–9	7–9	7–9	7–9
Alder & Rowan	6–9	2–3	2–3	2½–5	2½–5	6–8	7–9
Beech	5–7	0	0	0	0	1½–2½	2½–5

F = Felled

[6] Mottl, S., *A Case Against Damage by Deer* (Biologia, Prague, 1957).

Vegetation in any given area depends to a large degree on the geophysical conditions of the area: climate, soil structure, water and height above sea level, and is influenced by a variety of operations from draining to irrigation, and fertilising to sowing and planting. These operations are aimed at influencing the structure of vegetation and are usually related to the business objectives of the owners. Forest planting itself is one such operation. Where there are secondary objectives, like deer and/or game management, some ancillary operations may be introduced to enhance the living conditions. When nature conservation, preservation, or restoration of the aesthetics of the countryside are the aim, other measures may be found appropriate and 'extras' incorporated into the overall plan.

Because the composition of the vegetation changes as the trees mature, it is necessary to view deer capacity and density as flexible, so it has to be adjusted to match the changing feeding, the damage vulnerability and therefore the tolerated capacity of the forest. That is what Mottl recognises in the table above, relating his concept to both the age and species of trees.

It follows that if deer and game are a part of the overall business plan for the forest, suitable and appropriate allowances need to be made for their needs.

Deer Density and Damage

Mottl is only one of the many forest scientists who address themselves to the question of the relationship between density of deer and deer damage; others are referred to and quoted in the Annex to this chapter. Between them there are various views, but they basically agree with each other on at least one major point: the higher the density of deer, the higher the incidence of damage, and importantly, the relationship is not a straight linear one, but is exponential. The differences between the researchers stem from their choice of a very large number of permutations of the variables which can be applied.

We see, for instance, that in some areas certain tree species attract deer, whilst in other locations deer show little interest in these species; this may be due to alternative sources of food, but it could also be an indication of different needs of the local deer. Here a role may be played by different planting espacement, for the greater the espacement the more light reaches the ground and better ground cover provides more food until the canopy closes over and much of the ground cover becomes dormant. Interestingly, the modern regime in Britain is for conifers to be planted at 2,200 trees/ha which equals a 2.1 m espacement and broadleaves at 1,100 trees/ha giving a 3 m espacement or even more. Under these regimes ground vegetation survival is much longer than at the old espacement of 1.5 m and 2 m respectively. This in itself makes the newer woodlands more attractive to deer and game.

As already has been suggested 'too many deer – too much damage' is the principle, however simple or complex it may be.

To resolve the question of how many is too many it is necessary to have at least some idea of the numbers of deer present and this means counting, or at least estimating, the population. We know that counting deer, even on the open hill, is subject to error; how much more difficult and open to error is counting in a forest! Indeed, counting in a forest is a proposition attracting manpower costs, but estimating deer is possible and is discussed in Chapter 2.1. All the methods of estimating provide an approximation and therefore an acceptance of a level of error. When the numbers of deer are high, an error of 100 or 200 may not be important, but when the numbers are low, an error of the same number may be crucial. If on 1,000 ha we have 200 deer and we have made an error of 20 or 30 it matters only a little, but if on the same area we have only 100 deer, an error of 20 or 30 becomes significant, and let us face it, it is not difficult to 'lose' 20 deer in a forest during the count. It is important therefore to adopt a method as reliable as is possible and practicable and to reduce errors by occasionally using perhaps more than one method and comparing the results.

The consequences of error are numerous. They undermine predictions of population, assessments of deer quality, incidence of damage in relation to density, including the size of cull needed to keep the population under control, all of which are important aspects of planning deer management in relation to the overall business plan for the forest.

* * *

So far in Britain we lack adequate quantified data on the effects of deer grazing and browsing on cultivated crops or on hill vegetation. Some research has been done under the auspices of the Nature Conservancy Council[7]. The information, however, relates mainly to juniper and birch, neither of which is a commercial crop. Thankfully other research on the subject is in progress and we can look forward to the published results; in the meantime we have to rely on research from abroad.

Observations by W. Lindeman[8], suggest that in general terms, in a forest which is of uniform age structure with a deer density of 2-2½ red deer to 100 ha, the level of expected damage to trees is as follows:

[7] Nature Conservancy Council, *Annual Report 1971* (HMSO).

[8] Lindeman, W., *Zeitschrift fur Weltforstwissenschaft* (Munich, 1968).

Fig.17

DAMAGE(*) TO TREES UNDER LOW DENSITY CONDITIONS

	Conifers	Mixed	Broadleaf
Stripping	5%	2%	.2%
Browsing	5–7%	1–3%	.1%

(*) 'Damage' in this sense means trees which have been subjected to stripping and browsing with defined lasting effects.

He also observes that, by the inclusion of feeding plots of around 1%-3% of the forest area (this includes grassed rides and access tracks) the damage level can be reduced by as much as 60%. Therefore in mixed and broadleaf forests it can be reduced to an insignificant level, whilst in conifers it can be reduced to about 1%-3% for both stripping and browsing.

In this context it is important, that in *The Broadleaf Review* of July 1990, an announcement was made that the Forestry Commission is to allow as grant-worthy, open spaces within new plantings of up to 20% of the intended forest area. Whilst these are landscaping allowances, feeding lawns and shrubberies can be regarded as 'landscaping'.

My own observations, conducted not scientifically but to a degree subjectively, suggest that the damage through browsing, fraying/threshing and stripping follows a certain pattern which is presented in a tabular form below. I have divided the levels of significant damage incidence to groups of: very high = over 50%, high = 25%-50%, and low = 15%-25%, and being more specific below the 15% level. 'Damage' is taken as having the same meaning as in Lindeman's observations. In my generalisation I divide trees into young and old – young being those where the leading shoots are within reach of the deer, whilst old are those where the leading shoot is higher than the deer's reach.

The percentage values of damage are not exact, they vary with tree species and the degree of available food from other vegetation. This is why Lindeman suggests that with feeding areas of 1%-3% of the total forest, damage through browsing, and marginally through fraying, can be significantly reduced. Furthermore, if shrubs are underplanted along the edges of the forest, fraying/threshing damage can be further reduced because deer will use shrubs for this purpose. As a rule of thumb, a decrease in deer density level by half should result in damage reduction of at least one half, but a reduction of density by 10-15% will probably have no more than a marginal effect.

The table does not apply to deer in captivity or where the sex ratio is in excess of 1 : 3 in favour of either sex.

Fig.18   DEER DAMAGE VERSUS DENSITY LEVELS

Density per 100 ha		RED DEER			ROE DEER	
		stripping	fraying	browsing	browsing	fraying
14	young	0	v.high	v.high	6–8%	high
	old	high	v.high	0	0	high
12	young	0	v.high	v.high	5–7%	high
	old	high	v.high	0	0	low
10	young	0	high	high	4–6%	low
	old	low	high	0	0	negligible
8	young	0	high	low	3–5%	4–6%
	old	8–10%	5–10%	0	0	negligible
6	young	0	5–8%	8–12%	4–4%	3–5%
	old	4–6%	3–7%	0	0	negligible
4	young	0	3–5%	4–6%	all	
	old	3–4%	2–3%	0	damage	
3	young	0	2–4%	3–5%	negligible	
	old	2%	2%	negligible		
2	young		2–3%	2–4%		
	old	below 2%	below 2%	negligible		

Density versus Damage

From what is shown in the Annex to this Chapter we see that most authors and authorities lean towards low densities when considering deer as inhabitants of the forest.

On the Scottish hill, densities of 12-18 red deer per 100 ha are common. At that level deer survive on the heather and the heather *seems* to survive under the cumulative grazing pressure of deer and sheep even though in some areas concern is being shown for the low level of heather regeneration. A similar density in a wooded area, especially a woodland where there is a mixture of structural classes as one can increasingly find in larger forests (from tree plantations to the felling stage), would not be acceptable because of the damage the deer would inflict. The Forestry Commission[9] mentions red deer densities in various forests, in classes at establishment and pre-thicket stage (between planting and 3 m high) from 2-8 per 1 km sq, at thicket stage 10-40 per 1 km sq, and falling to about 2 per 1 km sq at pre-felling and felling stage. All forests are coniferous. However, in the description of the dung group counting method of establishing the deer population (see page 92) forests which have densities ranging from 13-38 deer per 1 km sq are identified.

These differences in deer densities may illustrate variety of toleration levels related to tree species/age, structural classes, or, the variety of management approaches to the question of deer density. It may also be that the management lacks reliable information on the deer population level on which to build a rational management policy. Sadly, it is also

[9] Ratcliffe, Dr. P., *Deer in Upland Forest* FC Bulletin (HMSO, 1971).

possible that there is a lack of appreciation of the importance of deer density, be it on the open hill or in the forest, in relation to the feeding potential of the location. This lack of understanding may have been a contributory cause to the 1989 spring die-off of red deer in parts of Ross and elsewhere along the spinal line of the Highlands.

All works which are quoted in the Annex suggest densities lower than 4 red deer to 100 ha (1 km sq) as being the approximate levels if the management's objectives recognise deer as a secondary crop of the forest. This allows for the protection of the timber crop by imposing damage control through maintaining a low deer density.

Professor Wagenknecht,[10] recognising the need for low deer density levels, also quotes von Sieffke who develops the question further. Whilst accepting that low deer density will mean a low venison yield, Sieffke develops another source of income, woodland deer trophies. He relates the size of deer population *and* forest area for the generation of high quality antler development; Sieffke's recommended minimum areas needed to achieve high quality trophies are:

Red deer 2,000-6,200 ha; Fallow deer 300-1,000 ha; Roe deer 150-500 ha.

Sieffke's table of the minimum requirements are at the end of this Chapter.

Deer Damage and Density (after Dr. Ueckerman)[11]

Ueckerman devotes a lot of his studies of red deer damage to density and damage evaluation, and of particular interest may be the relationship between density and damage by stripping. He highlights the fact that there is a significant difference between stripping damage done in winter and summer; he sees two main reasons for this difference:

1. In winter the cambium layer does not carry sap, therefore the tree 'bleeds' less, there is also a lesser risk of infestation of the wounded tree by fungi or bacteria and viruses, before the healing process starts.
2. At the same time he indentifies the extent of damage as being greater in winter than it is in summer, and his index of this relationship, which is tree-species related, shows that summer damage is about 30% lower than winter damage.

He also classifies the trees into three groups according to their susceptibility to damage by stripping as follows:

Highly susceptible : Norway spruce, ash, sweet chestnut
Susceptible : Douglas fir, Weymouth pine, lime, Scots pine, beech, larch, maple
Not susceptible : silver fir, oak, alder

[10] Wagenknecht, Dr. E., *Rotwild* (Neuman–Neudam, Berlin, 1981).
[11] Ueckerman, Dr., *Wildstand Bewirtschaftung und Wildschaden Verhuttung beim Rotwild* (P. Parey, Hamburg, 1960).

Furthermore, he recognises the different structural classes of vulnerable species; for instance – spruce at 10-45 years, pine 5-15 exceptionally 20, beech 15-50, larch 4-8.

His observations and studies of 53 forestry areas of what was West Germany, also provide an interesting relationship between the quality of the environment (established by his evaluation of density points as shown in the Annex and the incidence of stripping as shown on the graph below).

Fig.19   DEER DAMAGE –
STRIPPING RELATED TO DENSITY

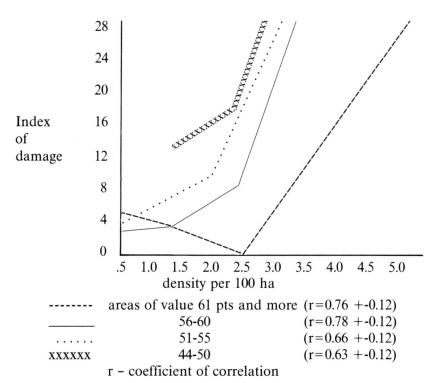

----------	areas of value 61 pts and more	(r=0.76 +-0.12)
_____	56-60	(r=0.78 +-0.12)
. . . . . .	51-55	(r=0.66 +-0.12)
xxxxxx	44-50	(r=0.63 +-0.12)

r – coefficient of correlation

The index figure = trees damaged by stripping in %.

NOTE:
The works of Lindeman, Mottl, Muller, Ueckerman and other Continental researchers were based in the main on German, and other Continental forests. Continental forests grow trees of different origins, living in different climatic conditions and controlled by different planting and felling regimes. In consequence the direct application of Continental research to British forests may be inappropriate. There are however lessons which could be adapted until British based research is completed.

Deer Density versus Animal Development

Clutton Brock,[12] relates that deer density affects the development of males and females to a different extent. As density increases, the mortality of juvenile males increases more rapidly than that of juvenile females, thus affecting the sex ratio. Also yearling stag antlers grow to a lesser length at high density. Generally, his supposition is that food deprivation has a greater effect on stags than hinds because of the greater need for energy food by stags at a young age. This observation may be more significant on the hill where food availability is often marginal.

Under woodland conditions food availability has probably the same effect but the scale must be different. Generally speaking there is more food available and in consequence woodland deer develop larger bodies and antlers than hill deer. This is especially important in broadleaf woodlands. Deer in dense (and often fenced) coniferous woodlands may find a less supportive habitat, perhaps even forcing them to migrate in search of food. In this respect it has to be remembered that the quality and quantity of feeding in conifer forests deteriorates rapidly once the canopy had closed. Such a change in the habitat may affect body and antler development.

Numbers – An Upsetting Influence

There are some serious, complicated and complex problems which so far have not been resolved and which are difficult to resolve by an individual. Some are not difficult – they are impossible!

In the context of this section the problem is the intrusion of deer from outside the owner's land.

The owner of an unfenced deer holding area, woodland or open hill, may spend significant resources in controlling his deer. He may even achieve the desired results in controlling his deer to the planned numbers, densities, sex ratio, and even quality when, out of the blue, other deer move in.

The facts are indisputable. In the first place deer are not adequately numerically controlled overall, they grow in numbers and spread. Where there were no deer yesterday, there are some now, where there were a few last year, there are many this year in spite of being controlled. Furthermore, by creating a more supportive habitat the survival rate is improved. There are of course other reasons, like land being fenced to contain or exclude deer thereby forcing deer to take to new habitats.

One can view a problem of this type in a selfish or altruistic way; on the one hand the intrusion of deer into the property from outside the boundary, on the other, the intrusion of deer from the area which is comparatively immune to damage to another area which is vulnerable.

[12] Clutton Brock, Dr.T.H. and others, *Red Deer in the Highlands* (BSP Professional Books, 1989).

The difference is perhaps of scale and the influence of the individual owner's controlling decision.

In reality, the answer to such a problem may be a bitter pill to swallow, calling for the commitment of additional resources to renewed control effort, and often softened only by the possible additional revenue gained from the increased cull which may be warranted. What really hurts however, is the sense of failure after efforts to control have been frustrated.

The only defence against being taken unaware is to keep one's eye open for the migration of deer, using what 'intelligence' there may be available, adjusting control measures immediately and keeping an eye on population dynamics, which with the improvement of habitat can also result in population increase.

These problems are easier to overcome by the creation of well planned Deer Management Groups which, through close co-operation between neighbouring owners, can become anticipatory rather than reactive.

*   *   *

In many large forest areas planted between the 1940s and 1970s, at espacements of half and less of the modern practice, deer (and game) have not been considered at the planning stage. In these forests, the numerical control of deer and the maintenance of low deer intensity levels of the order suggested in this Chapter and in the Annex, can probably be no more than a target setter; the reduction and adjustment of the deer populations to the necessary levels and structures may not be practical for many reasons. In these areas long term planning, probably reaching beyond the felling stage and into replanting, may be the only practical solution to a future rationalised deer population. In the short term the clearance of small feeding fields where culls can take place may be the only hope of achieving some sort of numerical control and deriving a revenue from marketing the venison.

In this work, which aims at improving the profitability of deer as a secondary product of forestry, accompanied by a reduction of damage to a tolerable level, and not at maximisation of the high value trophy profit opportunities, I usually use in the models densities of:

    Red deer   1 : 40 ha (25 head to 1,000 ha)
    Fallow deer   1 : 25 ha (40 head to 1,000 ha)
    Roe deer   1 : 15 ha (65 head to 1,000 ha)

The above densities are significantly lower than those often found in the British forests (significantly lower than the hill deer populations). They earn themselves a comment therefore, even by some authoritative sources, as being 'far too low for British conditions'. They are, however, related to the levels recommended by the authors quoted in the Annex, whereas many comments reflect practices established and enshrined in tradition and not within the framework of a progressive and rational deer management system appropriate to the forestry industry.

These densities can be achieved in longer term planning, and they result in the maintenance of low damage level and the production of improved quality of deer. The densities should be regarded as operational targets; they may have to be varied in recognition of local differences in vegetation, forest development stages, geophysical conditions and even the state of the 'deer market' where the demand may be for high quality trophies which require low densities, or a high yield of venison, calling for higher densities. All these factors may be influential.

Woodland Deer Density and the Neighbouring Farmland

We have concentrated on the woodland capacity, perhaps not noting that woodland deer will feed on adjoining cultivated land.

There are times in winter and spring when the crops, having germinated, produce a lush palatable ground cover. Deer will take advantage of this, paying particular attention to winter cereals and new grazing grass.

Grass consumed by deer is lost to the farmer, there is no argument about this; but the winter cereals, provided they are not trampled into the soil in wet weather, lose little of their vitality and ultimate crop bearing capacity.

The important consideration is that deer capacity calculations for the woodland need to take into account the surrounding cultivated land and that shortages of feed within the woodland will give rise to crop raiding, or marauding. The cultivated surroundings of the woodlands, which are not for the benefit of deer, must not be regarded therefore as an improvement of the feeding potential of the habitat allowing for more deer, but must be disregarded from the capacity calculation. (In this connection, using the Mottl coefficients as shown in the Annex page 80, item 6 in the model should not include in the evaluation those areas which are not grown for deer).

A certain amount of damage will take place on cultivated land when deer move their 'summer residence' to the cereal fields, where they form their couches and lie up for days on end, damaging some vegetation. Of more consequence are deer feeding on root crops, sugar beet being a special favourite of red deer.

Land Use and Density

When planning the future, or assessing the current deer density on a given area of land, or when considering the capacity of deer which can be tolerated, an important issue is the distribution of deer – 'land-utilisation' by deer.

By their habits or by human design, parts of the deer range are either completely 'unused' (e.g. blocks from which deer have been fenced out) or partially 'under-utilised' (e.g. rocky hilltops devoid of food and used by stags to escape from flies, or fields and grazing where deer are prevented or discouraged from feeding, but which adjoin the permanent habitat of deer). It is not logical to include the entirety of such areas in our calculation as a part of the deer range. It is more appropriate to include only that fraction of the area which represents the utilisation rate (e.g. if deer are estimated to use an area for two months a year, only one sixth of it should be included).

MacAuley Land Use Research Institute

Over the years the Institute has developed a model and programme for sheep stocking sustainable on the Scottish hills. Work is now in progress to reformulate the model and programme for red deer and it should be completed shortly. This is expected to be followed by similar models being developed for woodland and agricultural areas.

Fig.20   CRITERIA FOR TROPHY DEVELOPMENT
OF THE THREE MAIN DEER SPECIES

(After Sieffke as quoted by Wagenknecht)

		Red Deer	Fallow Deer	Roe Deer
Natural increase (spring count)		33%	35%	50%
Average venison boneless yield		65 kg	32 kg	12 kg
Early life weight increase per animal		21.5 kg	11.2 kg	6 kg
Age target		12 yrs	9 yrs	5 yrs
Population needed for trophy generation (minimum)		50	30	15
Recommended population density per 100 ha	a	0.8	3.0	3.0
	b	1.6	6.0	6.0
	c	2.5	10.0	10.0
Venison productivity per 10 ha in kg	a	17.0	34.0	18.0
	b	34.0	67.0	34.0
	c	54.0	112.0	60.0
Area required for trophy generation	a	6,200 ha	1,000 ha	500 ha
	b	3,100 ha	500 ha	250 ha
	c	2,000 ha	300 ha	150 ha

Yearly cull = natural increase.

Annotations: a = v.poor ground; b = good ground; c = v.good.

Annex to Chapter 1.5.
Evaluation of Density

If what has been said in the main body of this work about the relationship between deer density and damage is accepted, and if it is intended seriously to use control of deer density as a method of damage prevention, then it is essential that deer density is based on sound criteria. Regrettably there is little British research on the subject available to date, and therefore Continental material is used here, with all its shortcomings. Some Continentals admit that certain of their methods have not worked, they do not say, however, why this is so. Were the methods wrong or was the execution faulty?

The main factors which are repeated in most of the material are the origin of the forest (naturally regenerated, grown from seed or planted), location in relation to available feed, be this internally within the forest or by venturing into the surrounding agricultural land, geophysical conditions including rainfall and the severity of winters, the type and age of the forest and additional food (be it grown feed or provided only at times of natural food shortage). Other factors are the aims of deer quality and damage levels acceptable to the ownership.

Prof. Muller's Method[13]

The approach by Professor Muller relates the acceptable level of damage to the density of deer. Muller suggests that a damage level of 15% through browsing, and 5% attributable to fraying is acceptable because the recovery potential of the trees is significant and residual and permanent damage at these levels is tolerable even with the reduced subsequent value of timber. He examines the food potential of various species of trees, and differentiates between young and old, allotting coefficient values to each.

---

[13] Muller Using, *Grundlagen moderner Jagdwirtschaft* (Kroger, Hamburg, 1949).

Fig.21
FOREST CLASS (SPECIES/AGE)
FEEDING COEFFICIENTS

Species	1–5	6–10	11–20	21–40	41–60	61–80	81–100
	FOREST AGE						
Pine & Larch	50–70	5–25	0	10–26	30–50	45–65	45–65
Fir & Red Fir	40–60	40–60	0	0	0	25–45	45–65
Oak & Birch	60–80	60–80	35–55	50–70	55–75	55–75	60–80
Alder	50–70	15–25	15–25	20–40	20–40	45–65	55–75
Beech	40–60	0	0	0	0	10–20	20–40

Muller now relates the coefficients from the table above to the areas of each particular tree-species/age group, and applies the formula developed by Mottl[6]:

$$D = \frac{A \times C}{R}$$

Where D = density; A = area covered by each tree class; C = the coefficient for each class, R = total area of the range. He then applies the scores from Mottl's density table (page 81), but extends it to densities below those acceptable to Mottl:

Fig.22
RED DEER DENSITY SCALE

Density Points	Hectares per head of red deer
above 100	40
92-100	49- 40
85- 90	71- 49
41- 84	110- 71
31- 40	202-110
21- 30	243-202

Note:
  1 red deer = 2 fallow deer = 4-5 roe deer

S. Mottl's Method

Mottl himself produced a somewhat different method of estimating deer density, relating the type of ground vegetation providing the feeding base for deer to deer density, and also providing coefficients, which he then applies to the equation shown above.

Fig.23   NATURAL FEED – COEFFICIENTS OF VALUES

1. Area of bush, and lush scrub   179
2. Grass meadows in old deciduous woodland   78
3. Grass meadows in old conifer forests   65
4. Grass meadows in old mixed woods   66
5. Grass, woodland clearings or heath   48
6. Meadows, cultivation and other feeding
   areas within the range   56

Dr. H. Ueckerman's Method[11]

Ueckerman has established a method of calculating deer density at the optimum level (damage versus quality) by first classifying the deer habitat and then applying a points score to each. These scores are then converted to density levels.

A. Forests

Very Good Area. An area of complex in excess of 6,000 ha with small fields and meadows within. Fertile luscious ground cover including sweet grasses, fresh flowing water, mixed with broadleaf forest.

Good Area. A cut–up area of mixed forest predominantly conifer, some flowing water, undulating low hill country, few meadows and feeding areas, limited dense cover, good soil.

Poor Area. Sandy soil, dry or marshy land, heather and sour grasses (heather and sweet grasses are "Good"), peat, conifers, with moss undergrowth.

B. Field and Moorland

Very Good Area. Fertile cultivated land with a wide variety of crops, with spinneys of 25-40 ha.

Good Area. Mixed land, well watered, with scrub and spinneys below 25 ha, total area of deer range within 3,000 ha.

Poor Area. Sandy, moorland, mainly heather and dry sour grasses.

Ueckerman divides the land and allocates cultivation scores:

1. Percentage of forest within the range:

0	7 pts
1–20	8 pts
21–40	11 pts
41–60	13 pts
61–80	16 pts
81–100	18 pts

Meadows within the forest:

0%	9 pts
1– 4%	10 pts
5–10%	13 pts
11–20%	17 pts
over 21%	22 pts

2. Geology

Sandy downs	14 pts
Red sandstone	20 pts
Basalt & quartz	23 pts
Shale lime	35 pts
Glacial deposits	18 pts
Granite	20 pts
Oolitic limestone	30 pts

3. Afforestation

Spruces over 50%	10 pts
Pines over 50%	13 pts
Mixed forest	
3 types of trees	15 pts
Oak up to 30%	15 pts
Oak up to 40%	18 pts
Oak up to 50%	21 pts
Oak up to 60%	25 pts

Land itself is then scored

Very Good	71 pts
Good	61–70 pts
Medium	51–60 pts
Poor	41–50 pts

The total points from all tables can be equated to density figures below:
(density per 1000 ha)

	Roe Deer	Fallow Deer	Red Deer
40–45 pts	15	15–20	15
46–50	20	15–20	15
51–55	25	25–35	20
56–60	30	25–35	20
61–65	35	35–50	20
66–70	40	35–50	20
71–75	45	35–50	25
76–80	50	50–70	25
81–plus	55	50–70	25

It is interesting to note that in this method fallow deer are regarded as being closely density rated to roe deer. This may be a reflection of the fact that fallow deer are mainly grazers and as such cause only a limited amount of woodland damage, while red deer do not progress in the upper scores, their density remaining constant.

The last method, based solely on Ueckerman's land classification, has been developed by the author and is known as 'Playing Safe'.

HECTARES PER HEAD OF DEER

	Forest	Field	Moor
Very Good Area			
Red Deer	100	0	120
Fallow Deer	50	120	0
Roe Deer	20	60	40
Good Area			
Red Deer	200	0	160
Fallow Deer	70	160	0
Roe Deer	35	80	80
Poor Area			
Red Deer	300	0	200
Fallow Deer	100	240	0
Roe Deer	60	120	120

*   *   *

If the concept looks confounding when studying the models in the text or in this Annex, the results as they come out are even more so.

In the first place we are used in this country to talk of red deer in their thousands, or certainly hundreds, on a comparatively small area of land. In Scotland, the Scottish Landowners' Federation advocate no more than 1:30 acres (30 acres = 12 ha) as a guide to reducing the population of red deer on the hill thus confirming that it is often more. The hill of course is damage resistant until it becomes overgrazed (and in several places it is now, under the sheep and deer pressure).

In contrast the only other yardstick is an overall figure, applied to forestry in Hungary where the government regulates the population with a target of 1 deer to 76 ha, or six times sparser, with the Ueckerman model probably within striking distance of the same level. Both the Hungarian figure and Ueckerman's model accept a degree of damage and relate mainly to a self-generated forest, which is less damage prone.

At the other end of the scale (as devised by the models in the Annex), a forest which Ueckerman would score at 1 red deer to 76 ha would call for 50%-100% more ground per head, where the forest is damage sensitive. However, apart from the Scottish figure, all this applies to the Continent.

We need to develop a variant in order to recognise that our climate differs significantly from that of the Continent. They have hard, snowy and frosty winters, with deer sheltering in the forests. We suffer from higher rainfall, more winter gales, with chill factors of 0-5°C (above freezing) a high value which is critical for deer. Nor is our climate 'universal'. There are significant variations between north and south and west and east and these need to be reflected in the calculations.

There are also significant differences between Britain and the Continent in planting practices, the selection of tree species often leading to differing maturation times, which allows for different mixes and rates of development of ground growth (naturally regenerated trees or other ground cover plants). These differences also affect the deer feeding rates, providing different quality and quantities of food, which is especially important in deer regaining energy after the winter chills. One thing is absolutely certain, densities of the order we experience on the hills would cause untold damage to trees, young or old, and would lead to a high incidence of stripping and no number of feeding fields would change it.

Even the Hungarian 1 red deer : 76 ha is probably too dense a figure, allowing for the comparatively young and usually planted forests that we have in the UK. It would seem that something in the region of 1 : 100 would be about right if we were seeking a global flat figure giving our forests protection from damage. Much research will be needed in the years to come to establish more precisely a scale which could be defended in the UK with some degree of confidence.

1.6. Park and Open Range Deer

DEER PARKS are always popular with visitors; deer without much doubt are a public attraction and in parks open to the public are an enhancement of the park's assets. At the same time park deer are sometimes a headache and like deer farms, confuse the clarity of thinking about deer management.

Because a deer farmer can manage a hundred and more deer in a grazing paddock of a few acres, the naïve think that an area of a few acres, provided it is well fenced and grassed, is adequate for deer. Few appreciate that paddocks are rotated, that deer are heavily fed and that they are kept for a comparatively short time after which they are sold live or killed for venison.

Basically a red deer could survive on 2 kg of hay and 2 kg of roots per day but would not thrive on it.

The level to which deer require feeding a daily 'ration' to supplement the hard grazed grass in an often smallish park is in the order of 1 kg hay, ½ kg turnip, ½ kg silage – per day during summer[14], and 1 kg hay, ½ kg corn or maize, ½ kg dry clover or silage, with 2 kg turnip or beet, ¼ kg, with ¼ kg oats every two days in winter assuming minimum natural feed is available.

This 'prescription' for farmed deer highlights the difference between them and the open range deer, whilst the enclosed parks, many of them small and under-provided in natural food fall somewhere in between as far as deer feed is concerned. It should also be remembered that when feed additives are provided salt or other licks are usually needed to help deer to digest.

The requirement for fast body build-up which a deer farmer may have would call for feeding on manufactured feeds designed to build body and not fat.

In most parks deer have to be fed. There is a tendency either to stock densely to ensure a continuing and adequate attraction for the public, or if the park is run on a semi deer farm basis for venison and/or breeding high quality deer for live sales. Under the semi-farm conditions, additional feeding, above the winter ration quoted above may be called for.

[14]Fletcher, Dr. J., *Suggestions for Deer Park Managers from Deer Farmer* (BDS Symposium, 1988).

It is the general approach to feeding that is the major difference between management of captive deer and the open range animal.

Feeding of open range deer, other than during the few months of hard winter, is to a degree counter-productive. It is difficult to break wild deer to feeding on some kinds of dry fodder, manufactured cobs or similar. By the time they start taking the feed provided the need may have passed. It may be difficult to deliver feed to remote locations; additional feed stops deer from foraging for such food as nature provides, and encourages them to expect feeding. Whether it serves a purpose to feed a small proportion of the deer that are within easy access, and not to feed those in more difficult, less accessible locations is a point for debate.

Feeding to prevent stripping damage is to a degree different in principle (as suggested in Chapter 1.4). Completely different is the provision of feeding fields (lawns) for the deer to feed in throughout the year. This is a design feature to make a habitat 'deer friendly' – as is suggested in Chapter 2.6 and helps to prevent damage to valuable trees.

Feeding during times of need also to a degree upsets Nature's control mechanism by which an animal's metabolism is reduced and there is a reliance on the store of energy built up during the summer. The marginal exception might just be the roe deer, both sexes of which go through a period of active winter growth, the buck growing his antlers, the doe carrying her young. Here, during exceptionally hard winters feeding might be justified, accepting that there are significant difficulties in the choice of fodder, weather proof packaging and distribution. Of course it is unlikely that roe, as a matter of policy, would be managed as park deer, since they are almost impossible to farm.

Part Two

Methods

2.1. Counting and Estimating Deer Population

T HERE IS not much point in talking about deer densities and the relationship between density and damage levels if we do not know, at least approximately, how many deer we have to deal with in the first place. It does seem that numbers within a given property or even a part of it, be it agricultural, forestry or mixed are more often than not an enigma to the owner and his staff. An exception is probably the Scottish hills, where most owners have the deer counted either by their own staff or by the Red Deer Commission, or both, the latter counting the deer ranges in rotation, every few years. Even here little attention is being paid to concentrations of deer in small pockets, where overgrazing often results. Various techniques of estimating numbers were developed in the 1980s by the Forestry Commission and are being used on an ever increasing scale in the state owned and private forests where deer management is taken seriously.

In *Wild Deer*[1 & 5] and in *Deer Management*[15], the subject is broached and guidance is given to methods of counting and estimating the deer population both on the hill and in the forests. More recently, in Forestry Commission Bulletin 71[9], some excellent additional guidance is given, which, with the permission of the Commission, is described below.

Dr Ratcliffe suggests two approaches. One, known as the 'Vantage Point Count', is suited to hilly areas with good observation facilities; the other, the 'Dung Pellet Group Count', is more suited to flatter ground, perhaps densely afforested and used by the Forestry Commission in thicker, older forests. A version of the 'Vantage Point Count' is widely used by the Red Deer Commission on hills where the ground is suitable, as an alternative to a 'Team Count' and is described below.

Vantage Point Count

The method involves counting and recording deer from fixed observation points from which areas of 80-120 ha can be clearly observed. The observations are made over periods of 2-2½ hours at a time (thus allowing

---

[15] de Nahlik, A.J., *Deer Management* (David & Charles, 1974).

for rumination periods between feeds). The ideal time for observations is between 6.00 and 10.00 am and 4.00 and 8.00 pm, preferably in April and May; during these hours and in these months one can expect maximum deer activity.

During the observation, which needs to be exact and therefore requires binoculars or a telescope, recordings are made both on an accurate map of the forest block and in a log. On the map the precise location and identification of the deer (number, sex, age class, time of sightings and direction of movement) are recorded. Appearance and disappearance of beasts from and to cover is only recorded if there is no reasonable doubt that the same group, or individuals, has not been already counted. Hence group composition and the characteristics of the individuals are important indicators.

Three or four repeat counts are conducted over consecutive mornings and evenings, and fresh counts are conducted in adjacent areas of the different structural classes of forest. Repeat counts are conducted to overcome the problems of variation in deer activity due to changing conditions; the maximum number recorded in any single count period and in each location is accepted as representative of the structural class. Mean densities for each structural class are then applied to the forest area as a whole in relation to the component structural types present.

The deer density variations which can be expected in relation to the growth stages of conifers are shown below:

Fig.24

DEER DENSITIES – SELECTED SCOTTISH FORESTS AT DIFFERENT GROWTH STAGES

Forest Structure	Deer Density (No/1 km sq)		
	Galloway	Glenbranter	Glencripesdale
Establishment	2	2	–
Pre-thicket	5	8	–
Thicket	10	12	40
Pre-felling	2	2	–
Checked-growth	2	2	–

(From FC Pamphlet 71[9]. Density values obtained by means of Vantage Point Counts).

Simultaneous Observation

Similar in concept but somewhat different in execution, is simultaneous observation by a number of observers located at a number of vantage points.

The main idea is that the observations are in comparatively small woodland areas where, because of the woodland planning layout, it can be assumed that it is possible to see most, if not all, the animals in the woodland, or a specific part of the woodland which represents the identified habitually used territory. Depending on size, observation is made from one, two or if need be more vantage points, taking care that the dispersion and location of neighbouring observers is selected so that they do not 'spoil' the ground for each other, and that the animals seen by one observer are sufficiently 'localised' to be unlikely to venture into the observation area of another. As in the vantage point method, observations are made over two or three days on a sequence of mornings or evenings. One can assume that the highest number of deer recorded and identified on any one occasion from any one point (with reasonable assurance of no double counting) is the actual estimate of deer in that location. In most instances, however, when estimating roe or fallow deer a correction factor of up to 5-10% addition is needed even when experienced observers are used. The correction factor needs to be much higher, even double, if allowance is to be made for inexperienced observers, who on one hand may be prone to double counting, and on the other may not spot all the deer movements.

If the dispersion of observers is large, use of the sampling method for establishing the total population as for the Vantage Point Count is necessary, making sure that due regard is paid to the structural class differences between the woodlands.

Individual Observation

The same approach can be used by one person observing, taking each location at a time, but for practical reasons cutting the frequency to one or two mornings and evenings at each point, then moving to the next location. In this instance an error of 25-50% has to be accepted even if an experienced person is conducting the estimation.

Vantage Point Count – Hill Deer

The vantage point observation method is widely used by the Red Deer Commission for counting deer on the hill. The observer, located in a vantage point on a slope one side of a glen, counts and records deer on the opposite slope. Sometimes a helper is needed to move the deer from blind spots such as depressions in the terrain.

In using this method on the open hill sampling is not necessary provided the series of vantage points cover the entire range, neither is the selection of specific time of day important. Deer have no option but to be on the open hill and can be spotted when moving or resting, and in a sequence of observations the entire area can be counted.

Dung Pellet Group Count

(Based on Forestry Commission Bulletin 71[9], and Ratcliffe Dr. P., 'Roe Deer Management. The Application of Research', *Deer* (March 1989).)

While perhaps less precise as a method, the Dung Pellet Group Count is a useful method, especially where visual observation is not practical e.g. in very densely wooded areas, or areas where no suitable vantage points can be found. It stands to reason that there is a direct correlation between the number of deer and the density of dung pellets the deer leave, so a sample count of dung pellets can be used to estimate the number of deer.

A prerequisite is that the counters are able to distinguish between the pellets of different deer species and those of deer and other mammals. Deer pellets differ in size, colour and consistency depending on the diet, as well as the weather and season of the year. Accurate identification is necessary and to this end previously identified samples may be used as a guide. There is also a need to establish the rate of decay of defecations applicable to different locations. Decay is influenced by the type of food taken, the weather, as well as the co-habiting animals and insects for which the content of faecal pellets may represent a source of food and a suitable location for egg laying.

The area selected for the count should be of uniform structure, clearly identified on a block map. From an easily locatable spot on the perimeter a straight line inwards into the woodland is drawn as the 'Ground Survey Line'.

The direction of the survey line is recorded and this bearing is used when marching through the wood in a straight line with an orienteering compass. Along the line square plots of 7 x 7 m are laid on alternate sides, every 100 m, until eight plots are laid, using a tape measure for the size and a compass for right angles, the axis of the plot being the survey line. Each plot is searched, in bands one metre wide, for dung pellet groups and these are recorded. A pellet group is a cluster in excess of six pellets and includes 'strings' of pellets dropped by moving animals. Where pellets of different animals (of the same species) are found (marginally different sizes, age, appearance of pellets) the appropriate number of animals is recorded; where pellets are precisely on the edge of the plot, alternate groups only are counted.

The mean number of pellet groups per plot can be related to the range of population densities on the graph below. These densities apply only to the structural class of the forest in which the count was made; it follows therefore that counts have to be carried out in each constituent structural group before the total deer population can be ascertained. It is also necessary to ensure that the graph accommodates the dung decay rate appropriate to the location.

92

Fig.25

DUNG PELLET GROUP COUNT – DEER DENSITY GRAPH
(allowing for different rates of decay)
[after Ratcliffe]

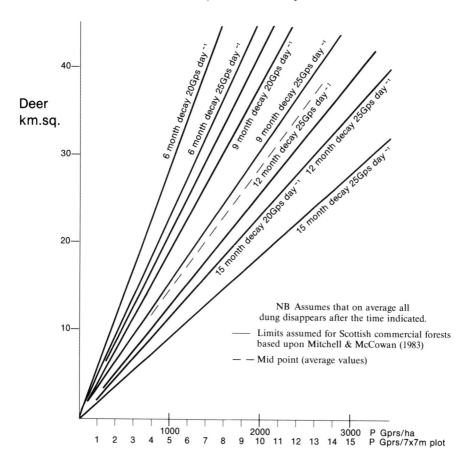

NB Assumes that on average all
dung disappears after the time indicated.

—— Limits assumed for Scottish commercial forests
based upon Mitchell & McCowan (1983)

— — Mid point (average values)

Note:
   With experience Dung Pellet Counts can be accurate. It is problematic
however whether an average woodland or forest owner would have the
resources of time and staff to use this method.)

Traditional Hill Counts

This method is only applicable to hill red deer (and maybe hill sika). No
other species habitually reside on the hill. Hill deer counts are usually
carried out in late February, March or April, when deer are in 'hard horn'
and when deer do not 'get lost' in the cover of bracken.

The method calls for a team of people (experienced with deer if possible) equipped with binoculars, maps, notebooks and pens, as well as a radio. The team is arranged in a line covering a wide front, but within visual distance of each other and each covering the neighbour's dead ground, moving forward and spying deer. All observations are recorded according to sex; calves are included as such. Deer movements are recorded and notified by radio or written down (time, composition of groups, direction of movement, appearance into sight or disappearance) to ensure against double counting.

There are two schools of thought. The Red Deer Commission counts deer only as they break through the advancing line of observers. To this end it is necessary for the teams to move down or across wind to encourage deer not to run ahead of the line but to break back. The other school records all deer seen and carefully analyses the records to take out all possible duplication.

Using the first method (RDC), the deer are dislodged from their habitual ground and there is possibly less risk of double counting but a greater risk of missing deer in dead ground, or of pushing deer over of the range boundary. Using the second method, unless meticulous analysis is made, double counting is a risk. There is also some advantage in counting deer in their habitual locations.

On large hill estates or management group areas several days may have to be devoted to hill counting, taking long sections of ground each day with each belt bordering on the one counted the previous day.

Moving Deer in Woodlands

A method of counting which has been successfully used in woodlands for some time, is that of moving deer to a line of observers/counters. In principle it is similar to driving a woodland for pheasants to a line of guns, the basic difference being that the beaters need to move slowly and quietly. Dogs have been successfully used to reduce the numbers of beaters needed, but they must be very steady and well trained. The deer move ahead of the beaters across an open area, like a ride, which is under the surveillance of observers/counters who record their sightings by sex and if possible a rough guide to age; calves are recorded separately. Rides or other observation areas must be wide enough to allow for accurate observation and recording of sightings. It is often necessary to have observers/counters in the flanking rides and even behind the beater team. Deer must be moved slowly and must not be allowed to stampede.

Again there are two schools of thought. One suggests that the direction of the drive should be arranged so that deer always move to the blocks already counted or free of deer (therefore calls for driving deer out of the first receiving block). Subsequent blocks are counted in succession. The other suggests that the block should be driven and counted, and the neighbouring block counted not less than 24 hours later, when the deer from the first block have returned to their original location. Some consider that the results are not sufficiently accurate to justify the manpower needed.

Tracks and Slots

The approach used for pellet group counting can also be applied to estimating deer numbers from tracks and slots. The method can only be used when slots are clearly visible and distinguishable, such as in snow, on wet ground or sandy soil.

The survey line is laid as explained previously, but always starting 5 m beyond the perimeter of the forest (deer often skirt the woodlands) and extending into it, crossing rides as far as the opposite edge of the wood, or in large forests being at least 600-800 m long. Along the survey line a 'corridor' is created – 1¼ m wide for roe, 1½ m for fallow and sika, and 1¾ m for red deer. The fresh slots of deer crossing the corridor are counted (and divided by four). One corridor is laid and counted in a forest block, of 500 ha, and two in forests of 1,000 ha. Spacing between the corridors needs to be at least 500 m, with the corridors running parallel to each other.

In undisturbed areas the results of the slot count within 24 hours of a fresh snow fall can be taken as the approximate number of deer within the area; where deer are disturbed by human or other activity interpretation is very difficult. With this method, which is not very accurate, at least a differentiation between 'many' and 'few' can be established.

Continuing Observation

Once deer numbers have been established and the population brought down to a manageable level, a different approach can be used, relying on simple observation and recording by those who, in the course of their work in the forest, have to carry out regular and frequent (say once a week) rounds of all locations. During the rounds all deer sightings are recorded on a map and in a log. This approach is particularly useful for recording the quality of beasts and the usual and preferred movement areas. Such observations can be taken from high seats, just as much as from the seat of a vehicle. It is important, however, to ascertain to what extent deer take to flight on sight of a vehicle and even more so upon the vehicle stopping and the engine being switched off.

For updating records of numbers and quality this is a manpower effective method, especially under conditions of low deer density such as is required for damage prevention. The method fails where the number of deer is high, movements are erratic or frequent and there is a high level of disturbance. At low densities and in parks the concept "My sheep know me and I know them" can be literally applied to deer; the characteristics of each beast can be quickly and effectively ascertained and remembered (or recorded). This means in turn that the development of each animal from year to year can be followed by a keen observer.

Small Deer Counting

The smaller the deer we are trying to manage the more difficult it is to establish with any degree of reliability their numbers. Many of us know how difficult (but not impossible) it is with roe deer. The problems with counting muntjac or Chinese water deer are infinitely greater, especially as these timid deer live in areas of thick brambles, herbs and grasses, and are almost invisible.

Simple Statistics for Population Forecasts

Another useful technique which can be used once the overall numbers have been reasonably accurately established is to approach the estimation statistically, using the basic data of population numbers, calving rates, cull numbers and mortality, natural and accidental. A statistical approach is also used for deer in other management records in Chapters 2.4 and 2.5.

It happens from time to time that even on estates where yearly counting of deer is practiced, the count goes wrong. It happens that the weather breaks and does not allow the count to be carried out. It is also common practice that, to save effort, an annual count is not done and therefore the management rely on an estimation of the deer population in order to plan the cull.

A simple approach to estimating and forecasting, derived from a firm data base, is illustrated in the model below. In this model certain assumptions are made:

a. There was a good deer count the previous year

b. The count established numbers of stags, hinds and calves

c. The calving rate is agreed as a best approximation based on previous years' counts (in this model 40% of all adult hinds at the March count)

d. Cull record is accurate

e. Natural mortality rate has been agreed at 5%

Fig.26   ESTIMATING DEER POPULATION

| | | Year 1 | | | Year 2 | |
	Stags	Hinds	Total	Stags	Hinds	Total
Adult population previous year	400	500	900	374	437	811
Less culled last season	80	110	190	90	125	215
= Adult population at end of season	320	390	710	284	312	596
Plus Calves previous March (counted* or 40% of hinds**)	88*	90*	178*	62	62	124**
Less Calves culled	15	20	35	21	19	40
Adult population this season	393	460	853	325	355	680
Less 5% mortality	19	23	42	16	18	34
Population forecast (adult)	374	437	811	309	337	646
(calves)	73	70	143			

Note:
Year 1 is based on actual information. Year 2 starts with a sum of Year 1 activity, and continues with estimates based on known rates of calving, mortality etc.

It should be possible from simple ongoing observation throughout the year to ascertain whether deer numbers are static, increasing or decreasing, without necessarily resorting to a full counting process which may be manpower costly. Recorded indices of deer damage from year to year also provide an independent and reasonable indication of deer population and density trends (see also Chapter 2.5).

It is difficult to be precise about the desired frequency of formal counting; annually would be ideal but possibly considered expensive in terms of manpower. Once accurate data is established yearly counting could be dispensed with and the statistical approach based on the model above can be used. Gaps in excess of five years between counts should be regarded, however, as too long.

Accuracy in Deer Management

Deer Population and Age

The more one gets involved in discussions on management of deer the more conflicting opinions one encounters. Many of these opinions are good and constructive, some are in my opinion not so good.

In management of deer, especially deer in the open range, it is necessary to resort to practical experimentation. By this I mean asking the question 'what happens if. . .?' and trying it out, as opposed to scientific experimentation where the question of 'what happens if. . .?' is followed by a study of alternatives, setting up controlled and comparative trials, backed by computer models, new brains and new methods.

We have several examples of these different approaches in deer management and some of the views held tend to deter those responsible for deer from taking action.

I will start with 'ageing' deer.

It is generally accepted that recording the age of culled deer is important for a variety of reasons. What is disputed however is the method used. The simple method of assessing age by tooth eruption and wear is no more than an approximation and tooth sectioning is laborious and slow and therefore not practical under working conditions.

'Deer counting' is like a nest of vipers – tread carefully! In the first place we have to accept that 'counting' is perhaps not a good word for it has connotations with the precise science of mathematics, where a number, any number has an absolute value and there are no 'arguments'. Deer counting is at best an approximation – even the 'scientific' methods.

Several methods of counting deer have been described in this chapter.

The first must be the comparatively precise scientific approach of the Dung Pellet Group Count. The basic methodology is not too complex, but it is manpower costly. Correctly conducted, the results are acceptably accurate. A far less accurate method, similar in concept, but not scientifically acceptable, is counting deer slots. Another accurate, but less scientific method accepted by many scientists, is the Vantage Point Count. Similar in some respects is simultaneous observation from a number of vantage points, or individual observation from a number of vantage points, taking locations in sequence and allowing for 'adjustments'.

The typical hill deer count with a number of counters walking in line is one of the more accurate methods when carried out by experienced teams. Similar to the hill count method is that of moving deer in woodlands through a line of counters positioned in good viewing positions, such as wide rides, river banks, and feed fields. Both methods are manpower costly, but usually large areas can be covered in a comparatively short time. Needless to say, hill counting as described above is far more accurate than moving deer through the forest, especially where it is close planted and the rides narrow or very widely dispersed.

Finally we can rely on local foresters, stalkers and keepers who have some knowledge of deer and of keeping records.

* * *

In the search for a more precise way of confirming deer counts the cohort analysis method has been developed (page 102). In itself it is accurate, but only in defining the possible minimum deer numbers and it does so historically. It calls however for a precise ageing of dead deer, which is difficult to achieve in practice.

In both ageing and counting many say that, although practical, these methods are invalidated by the lack of accuracy. Nothing is further from truth – in all planning some information is better than none, so long as the information is not misleading.

Deer are culled for a number of reasons: to maintain numbers at a given level, to reduce (control) damage, to improve quality etc.

Let us assume that, using whichever method of counting, we arrive at a certain level of deer population. Let us then say that at that level we have poor trophies, or low recruitment, or too much damage. As a result we must make a management decision to increase the cull and reduce the population. Each year we count our deer using the same method. By using the same method (and the same people) we can assume that the margin of error is consistent from year to year. Therefore if we find a reduction in numbers counted, we can safely assume that the population is dropping (or *vice versa*). We can confirm this by looking for the other corresponding and sequential changes: lower damage rate, increased calving rate, better trophies, better body-weight. As long as these changes are not evident (bearing in mind that some are very slow in becoming apparent) the cull rate is insufficient. In all this we have to note that population changes are not usually solely related to calving but can be affected by migration, mass deaths, poaching and disturbance of all sorts including the introduction of domestic stock to the deer range.

It can be said, that what we are looking for in much of our deer related 'number crunching' is not absolute accuracy but trends; the trends in deer population and their effect on the habitat and our crops, and the corresponding trends in changes of quality.

Such trends can be clearly visible if well presented; no one could miss the trend demonstrated by the deer population graph (page 100).

Fig.27   GRAPHICAL PRESENTATION OF
RED DEER POPULATION RECORD

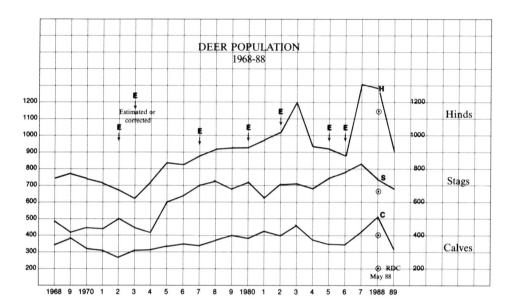

Cull and Density

So far we have posed questions regarding the numerical accuracy of our deer count, the estimation of numbers if you prefer, and ageing. We can say that in relation to ageing we need to develop some accuracy if we wish to cull trophy beasts at the right age. The quarry must attain an age at which its development has reached a plateau and when trophies are ready for harvest. To this end age-banding is sufficient. We have also seen that to present the cohort analysis an accurate ageing method is needed.

Population size is, however, more enigmatic. Some people consider that it is of only academic interest and therefore not worth the effort of addressing it seriously. Indeed, so unimportant is it to them, that they discard the very concept, especially in relation to woodland deer, finding it so difficult to establish and so manpower consuming as not to be worth the effort. In its absence they establish their culling level by trial and error, perhaps looking for established trends in deer damage, or occasional and subjectively evaluated sightings, and adjusting the cull in relation to damage, or perhaps going by 'feel' of numbers derived from an almost subconscious correlation between deer sightings and a concept of total population, often without putting a numerical value on it. To this end they may, for instance, increase the cull and monitor the changes in damage intensity and if damage is still at too high a level increase the cull

100

further. This way they do not know how many deer they ought to cull in relation to the natural increase needed to maintain a static population (without establishing the number of females and the female to young ratio they cannot know the size of natural increase).

This disregard of the importance of deer population size is attributable to the fact that the issue of deer density and capacity is not well understood and therefore the matter of establishing the size of cull in relation to deer population and the habitat's 'deer capacity' is still not a generally accepted practice.

Once the culling related to capacity principle is accepted as a managerial policy requirement then all aspects of population dynamics need to be recognised and reflected in the cull levels.

This does not mean that accurate counts need to be done every year. It is possible to develop a simple arithmetical model as detailed earlier in this chapter. This does not require a computer; the data can be handled with basic mathematical skills.

We can now superimpose on the population graph accurate information from a succession of culls, and see how the whole story presents itself, even to the non-statistician.

Fig.28　　　　GRAPHICAL PRESENTATION OF
RED DEER POPULATION AND CULL

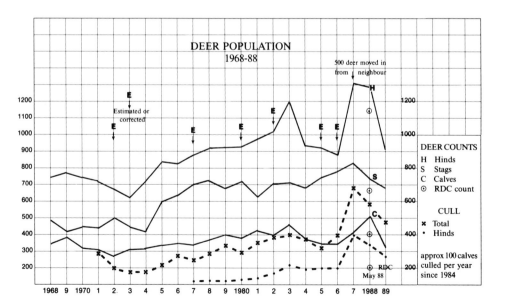

Cohort Analysis*

Cohort analysis is a method of establishing deer population retrospectively from past cull records. All cull records need to include accurate ages of beasts shot or found dead. In this way each year's cull can be analysed, each beast killed being allocated to its year of birth.

After a number of years, a period which has to be longer than the average life span of the local deer, each year's cohort (a collective name for all animals born in the same year) is calculated as the minimum number of deer that were born that year. This number can then be translated into the number of females required to produce that number of offspring, provided that calving rates for the locality are also known.

If the sex ratio is known it is also possible to arrive at the estimated number of males. The reconstructed population figures can in turn be compared with the deer counts (or estimates of population) to ascertain their accuracy. The margin of the established past errors can be applied to current deer counts as a correcting factor.

The use of cohort analysis is only possible if deer ageing is absolutely accurate; done by tooth section and not by eruption and wear. Difficulty in finding beasts lost to natural causes, poaching, and possibly road traffic accidents may influence the effectiveness of the analysis.

Fig.29　　　　　COHORT ANALYSIS - ROE DEER

COHORT	CULL YEAR										AGE	No.SHOT FROM COHORT
	1982/3	1983/4	1984/5	1985/6	1986/7	1987/8	1988/9	1989/90	1990/1	1991/2		
1982	1	1	1	2	1	0	1	0	0	0	10	2
1983	2	1	2	1	1	2	1	2	0	0	9	13
1984		2	1	2	4	2	4	4	2	1	8	22
1985			2	2	3	6	2	3	6	7	7	31
1986				3	3	3	3	2	1	3	6	19
1987					2	3	1	3	4	2	5	15
1988						2	1	2	3	2	4	10
1989							3	2	3	5	3	13
1990								0	0	2	2	2
1991									3	4	1	7
1992										3	0	3
TOTAL CULL								18	22	29		

↑　　↑　　↑

Yearly　culls

*based on Ratcliffe[9].

2.2. Age Calculation by Teeth and Bone Formation

T HE ABILITY to estimate age by body shape as described earlier (pages 16-18) may be of assistance when out deer stalking or establishing the 'shootability' of a specific deer; indeed, it is indispensable for the correct apportioning of animals to age groups and for successful management planning. Regardless of experience this is a far from easy task and even the most knowledgeable stalkers make mistakes. However, it is possible to estimate the age of a dead beast more accurately; firstly by tooth wear, secondly by the condition of the central seam of the skull frontal bones and thirdly by the shape of the bone formation of the pedicle. Tooth wear is the most accurate – the other two methods can be used to establish only an approximate age and are useful if the teeth have been damaged or are not available for inspection. Knowledge of tooth wear as well as acquaintance with other methods of ageing is therefore important to managers and stalkers.

Tooth wear varies from species to species and is linked to the longevity of the animal. In roe, which have a shorter life span than red deer, wear is fastest. In the longer living fallow, sika and red, tooth wear is slower. It also varies according to locality and the stalker needs to be aware of local patterns of wear.

Allowance must also be made for the hardness of the teeth and type of food the animal finds in its habitat. The hardness of the food available and the type of abrasive deposits, such as sand and other mineral dust, affect wear.

Tooth growth in the first three months of life consists of the four front and three cheek teeth on each side of the lower jaw, which are all milk teeth. The upper jaw contains only three cheek teeth. These teeth are similar in all three species of deer.

For the purpose of age calculation, we will interest ourselves particularly in the eruption of milk teeth and the wear of the permanent cheek or molar teeth of the lower jaw. The front teeth do show age, but they differ so considerably from area to area, depending on the type of food, that general knowledge of them is insufficient without an intimate knowledge of the particular locality, which may be as small as one particular block of the forest.

The cheek teeth of the lower jaw are divided into premolars (the first three) and molars (the last three). Of these the three premolars are the first to grow.

Fig.30 DEVELOPMENT OF TEETH OF THE LOWER JAW

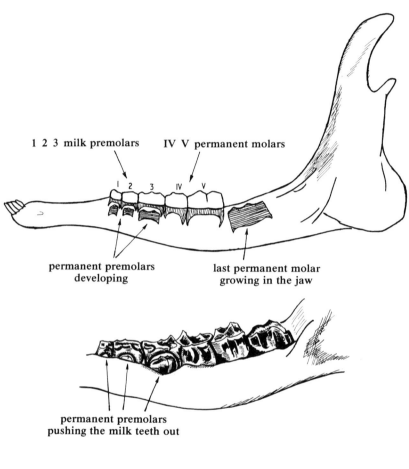

permanent premolars
pushing the milk teeth out

full set of permanent teeth
(Roe deer at 13 months, Red deer at 30 months)

LOWER JAW DEVELOPMENT

	Roe Deer			Red Deer		
Age	*Incisors and canine*	*Premolars**	*Molars**	*Incisors and canine*	*Premolars**	*Molars**
1 month	all milk	1, 2, 3	—	all milk	—	—
4 months	all milk	1, 2, 3	IV	all milk	1, 2, 3	—
6 months	all milk	1, 2, 3	IV, V			
8 months	1st perm	1, 2, 3	IV, V	all milk	1, 2, 3	IV
10 months	2nd perm	1, 2, 3	IV, V			
13 months	all perm	I, II, III	IV, V, VI	all milk	1, 2, 3	IV, V
1¼ years				1st perm	1, 2, 3	IV, V
1½ years				2nd perm	1, 2, 3	IV, V
2 years				all perm	1, 2, 3	IV, V
2½ years				all perm	I, II, III	IV, V, VI

* Arabic numerals denote milk teeth, roman numerals permanent teeth.

The first molar is the first permanent tooth to grow, and as the jaw-bone elongates with the animal's development so the other two molars follow when space is available for them. The second and third molars appear when the premolars are still milk teeth. In roe deer, the three molars are usually grown by the time the animal is about 12 months old, though the growth of the third may be delayed, sometimes by two months. In red, fallow and sika deer the third often does not appear before the 18th month.

The secondary premolars appear after at least two of the molars are grown.

In the primary (milk) growth the second and third premolars are different from the permanent teeth. They look as if they consist of more than one tooth, and this is particularly marked in the third premolar, the second milk premolar may appear to be of two teeth, the third often three. The division in the first often does not appear except at the root. Permanent premolars are more solid in appearance. The first looks single, so does the second, while the third looks as if it consists of one large and one small tooth.

A full set of permanent teeth in roe deer is completed sometime between the 12th and 14th month, in red, fallow and sika often as late as the 30th, and the small muntjac is roughly the same as the large deer.

All teeth are subject to wear but it is on the central part of the jaw affecting the third premolar and first and second molars that most of our age estimating is based. Their wear is gradual and continues until they are practically destroyed.

With advancing age the saw-like edge of the biting surfaces is worn down. The saw-edge line on the inside of the teeth remains sharp for some time but the height of the teeth above the gum line decreases and the chewing surfaces from being rough in youth become smooth and hollow-ground. As the wearing down of tooth surfaces continues the register in the teeth loses its depth until the surface is smooth and less able to grind the food and cud.

From the age of four in roe deer and eight in the large species the saw-edge on the premolars almost vanishes. The rounding off of the molars comes four years later and the gradual wearing down continues, until the beast is unable to chew its cud and dies of starvation or other digestive upset.

In areas where deer are short of minerals it is not uncommon for the stage of wear normally reached from the age of 12 onwards in red, sika and fallow deer, and seven onwards in roe, to be accelerated and general decay of the teeth sets in. Normally this can be recognised by the fact that all the teeth are being worn down and the deterioration which is normally more advanced in the third premolar (III) and the first molar (IV) is almost equalled in the other teeth, possibly with the exception of the first and second premolars (I, II). Animals feeding mainly on the field and soft woodland crops retain their teeth longer than those on the hills.

Many experts place great emphasis on the wear of the third molar (the last tooth at the back of the bottom jaw), which is of treble build, the last section being high and narrow. This tooth is fully developed when the large species are 30 months old and roe deer about 18 months. From this age onwards the high and narrow section is subject to gradual, regular and continuous wear, thus giving a good indication of age.

Fig.31   TOOTH WEAR AGE ESTIMATION BY THE
THIRD MOLAR AND THIRD PREMOLAR/FIRST MOLAR

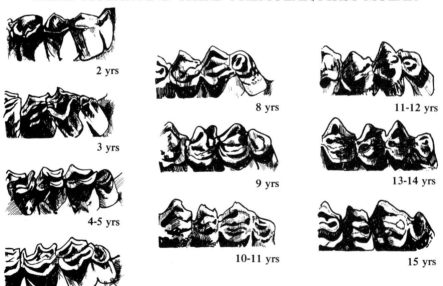

2 yrs

3 yrs

4-5 yrs

6-7 yrs

8 yrs

9 yrs

10-11 yrs

11-12 yrs

13-14 yrs

15 yrs

106

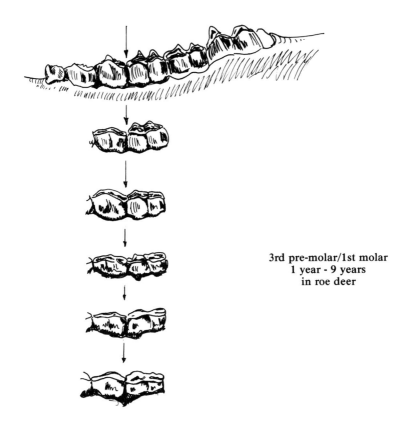

3rd pre-molar/1st molar
1 year - 9 years
in roe deer

All these methods are valid, but all have to be used with some circumspection. Ideally every indication should be considered, and this is why, when attempting to estimate age the entire jaw-bone (both sides) should be used. Occasionally access to the upper bone may reveal reasons for unusual wear in some teeth.

In Britain, work on the applicability of various methods of age estimation to Scottish deer, using material from deer of known age, began in late 1950s (Lowe,[16] 1967; Mitchell[17], 1963, 1967).

The outcome was the development of a method based on growth layers in dental cement, which grows around the roots of all teeth and also forms a thick pad below the crowns on each molar. Although these layers when sectioned are a little easier to expose and interpret than those of dentine, neither method is convenient for routine practical management purposes. The main values of this technique are in research or in checking other methods of age estimation.

[16] Lowe, V.P., *Teeth as indication of age* (Journal of Zoo No.152).

[17] Mitchell, Dr. B., *Determination of age in Scottish red deer from layers of dental cement* (Journal of Animal Ecology No.36, & RDC).

PLATE 7 CROSS SECTION THROUGH DENTINE PAD

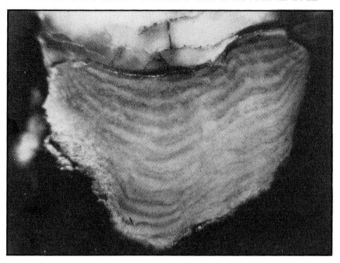

(after Mitchell[18]) (*by permission of Red Deer Commission*)

Skull Bones

The first sign of age appears in the centre seam of the skull frontal bone. This seam is well defined in the young head and in a dried skull-bone a certain amount of movement between the two skull cupola may be felt. With age, however, the cupola grow together along the seam until at an advanced age (seven to nine years in roe and fourteen to seventeen in large deer) the seam almost disappears, the two halves virtually coalescent.

Calculation of age by means of the skull pedicles is based on the fact that at an early age these are thin and the extensions running down towards the eye sockets are well defined. The pedicles on the inside of the antlers form a well-defined groove, with the skull bisection through which it appears in the shape of the letter V, slightly sloping inwards, so that one arm (the inside of the pedicle) is almost vertical. The skull seam falls where two oblique arms of the V's cross. From the age of three in roe, and four to five in large deer, these well-defined parts of the pedicles start to disappear. The extension running towards the eye-socket increases its circumference and thus flattens and ceases to stand out from the skull-bone.

The inner parts of the pedicles 'grow-in' into the skull, the base spreading until the two pedicles between them form a letter U the centre of which rests on the centre seam.

Neither of these systems is sufficiently accurate to allow for more than a 'feel' of age. The pedicle in muntjac is so different in its configuration that the descriptions above do not apply.

[18] Red Deer Commission, *Red Deer Management* (HMSO, 1981. Contribution by Dr. B. Mitchell).

Annex to Chapter 2.2.

Illustrations of Other Age Indicators

Fig.32

AGE INDICATORS
ANTLER AND PEDICLE

$$A_1 = A_2$$
$$B_1 < B_2$$
$$C_1 \leqslant C_2$$

Thickness of pedicles:
left young, right old.
Note also the frontal
bone seam coalescing.

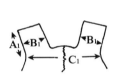

Coroncts, from the left:
'rolled up' – young,
'drum' – mid-age,
'drooping' – old.

Large deer, Brow:
Left – young,
Right – drooping at base – old.

Pedicle Indications
(After Bubenik[19])

Several writers and students of antler development, have produced a
formula for calculating age from pedicle measurements, derived from the
mean of diameters of poth pedicles (D) measured where the pedicles are
thinnest, and mean of the lengths (L):

$$Age = (D \times 10) \div L$$

[19] Bubenik, A., *Das Geweih* (P. Parey, Verlag, Hamburg, 1966).

There is a need for an adjustment of the result which differs between roe deer and other deer:

Roe deer: results 2½ to 7½ years deduct 1 year
                    over 7½ years no adjustment.

Other deer: results 3 to 8½ years deduct 1 year
                    9 to 16 years no adjustment
                  over 16 years deduct 2 years

Fig.33   AGE INDICATORS – TOOTH REGISTER WEAR
(3rd premolar)

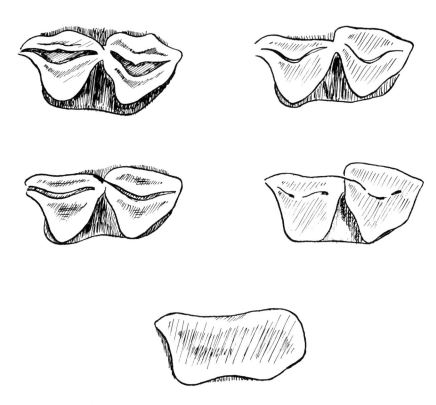

Tooth register:
open when young – left top,
completely worn down when v. old – bottom.

2.3. Cull Planning

THERE ARE a variety of ways in which people managing deer approach the cull planning task. To a degree they are guided by the overall strategy and objectives set by the owner or the management and within the constraints of the habitat in which the cull is to be executed. At the same time, there are many others whose plans are, so to speak, retrospective; they cull, then by monitoring the results or effects introduce changes to their cull accordingly without a long-term plan.

If the single and only objective, long and short-term, is to reduce the deer population to a minimum, the cull calls for the maximum numbers possible. The plan is fairly straight forward: cull as many as is practical, and certainly cull as many females as possible to reduce the natural increase. There is another ruthless cull plan, which must be condemned in deer management philosophy, and that is to select and cull all the best beasts, get as much 'satisfaction' or profit from them as possible and then get the hell out. Neither approach is worthy of the label 'deer management cull plan'.

In every business there is a need to plan; to plan the targets to be reached, the methods by which they can be achieved and the resources needed to make this possible. There is no reason why deer and habitat management should be any different. In this planning we must not lose sight of the fact that there are certain things which might be 'nice' to carry out but which are impossible or impractical. It may be, for instance, impossible and impractical to achieve significant changes in body-weights under given habitat conditions and the same may apply to the improvement of trophies. It is not possible, without commitment of extravagant resources to manage, in the full sense of the word, muntjac populations other than to keep numbers under control. Many believe that the same applies to roe deer, although significant results have been obtained by the application of management methods to roe. Planning the cull is therefore an important function; after all even conscious and logically justified decisions to do nothing, or to concentrate on harsh numerical control, are tactical if not strategic plans.

In a rational deer management cull plan and its execution there are two distinct phases:

Phase 1 – the initial setting up of a rational level of deer population to reach the desired, acceptable density. In this phase, while the prime objective is numerical reduction, it may be possible to also adjust the sex ratio to the desired level.

Phase 2 – the maintenance phase starts when the required level of population has been reached and efforts can be aimed at maintaining that level. One can then attempt to reach other objectives, usually rationalising the age structure, fine tuning the sex structure and improving quality through careful selective culling.

The first requirement therefore, in planning a maintenance cull is to be aware of the management objectives for the deer population.

There are some owners, primarily of hill deer forests, who aim at maintaining the population in such a manner that they optimise the venison yield. In this situation the sex ratio must be highly geared, probably at a level of three to one, hinds to stags. With this policy the age structure is a young one, simply because with high numbers of females and therefore a high level of annual increase the population level cannot be sensibly maintained with a high number of old beasts. The major quality consideration is that of venison, more than of antlers, with the maintenance of the habitat biased towards venison production.

It goes without saying that:

a. There are some species of deer which do not suit the 'venison policy'. Firstly, on account of their size, the smaller deer, roe, muntjac and Chinese water deer are unsuitable. Secondly, because of practical culling difficulties, woodland deer should not be managed at such a highly geared sex ratio. Achievement of a high female cull may be problematic, and failure would spell the danger of a population explosion.

b. The management of muntjac and Chinese water deer (some would add roe deer) does not lend itself to full scale 'management' as envisaged here, beyond numerical control perhaps related to the containment of damage. (In the author's opinion roe deer are too valuable an asset to be written-off in this way).

c. Because of (a) above, in the main, only hill red deer can be managed at a highly geared sex ratio, where culling is comparatively easy.

For these reasons we are primarily addressing here conditions where management objectives lend themselves to maintaining the population at a sex ratio of 1 : 1 or thereabouts and therefore where deer are numerically controlled at a predetermined level with:

1. Containment of damage.

2. Optimisation (not maximisation) of the venison yield.

3. Optimisation of returns from sporting letting.

4. Improvement of quality of trophies.

It is fortuitous that these objectives are complementary and mutually supportive.

In this approach a significantly important factor is the consideration of age structure. The aim is to maintain the deer population so that males reach an age just past maximum antler development and the females are no older than the peak of good motherhood. Because these ages vary between locations, being dependent on the quality of the habitat, it is impossible to be precise and one has to generalise:

	Red Deer	Fallow Deer	Sika Deer	Roe Deer
Males (age yrs)	11–15	9–12	9–12	6–8
Females (age yrs)	7–9	7–9	7–9	6–7

In a similar manner one has to address the natural increase. Again there are local differences linked to habitat quality. Here we are not talking of the natural increase in absolute terms but of 'post-first-winter survival' – that is after the yearlings have been exposed to one season's culling and to winter mortality.

The local differences can be summarised as follows:

	Red	Fallow	Sika	Roe
Post-winter female to young ratio	30–50%*	45–60%	40–60%	60–100%

* 30–40% is appropriate to hill deer; woodland deer can reach over 50%

This information, together with the total number of deer to be maintained and the locally applicable age structure, forms the skeleton of cull planning.

Whether one likes it or not, the Hoffman Pyramid approach to cull planning is probably the simplest rational method of presenting the deer population and cull. This is described in detail later in this chapter.

It often happens that during the first phase (numerical reduction), beasts of a certain age bracket have been overshot, and the maintenance cull needs to recognise this and be easy on the numerically low age-bracket.

In the cull plan it should be recognised that culling through the age-bands should be rational. A suggested allocation of cull percentages to age-bands is shown on page 114.

Fig.34   CULL RELATED TO AGE BANDS

RED DEER

Age band	Population structure	Cull structure* % Of population	% Of cull
10–14 yrs	15%	3–4%	15–20%
5– 9 yrs	30%	2–3%	10–15%
1– 4 yrs	35%	5–6%	25–30%
calves	20%	8–9%	40–45%

ROE DEER

Age band	Population structure	Cull structure* % Of polulation	% Of cull
6–7 yrs	10–15%	4–5%	13–16%
3–5 yrs	15–20%	5–6%	16–20%
1–2 yrs	40%	6–7%	20–24%
kids	30%	13–14%	44–47%

* includes losses due to non-cull mortality

Notes:
1. The structure for red deer can also be used for fallow and sika.
2. Apply this structure as a guide to the age related count results and work out what numbers of beasts in each age band (see Hoffman Pyramid) should be culled.

Monitoring Results

In drawing up the yearly cull plan it is important to measure the results of the execution of the culls of preceding years and analyse any changes in quality. Quality changes can be imperceptible from year to year. They can be affected by freak climatic conditions; the weather affecting the supply of food or chilling the beasts with resulting losses of energy fat. Gradual changes in antler quality, average weight and calving rates are identified only through meticulous recording from year to year and careful analysis by comparing the records.

For these reasons the plan and its execution has to include careful recording of changes, which will hopefully show the following improvements:

1. Antlers – changes which sooner or later will result in better quality stags and bucks on reaching the age of 'harvest' as fee-worthy trophies.
2. Weight increases – improving venison yields and healthier females better able to produce superior offspring with an increased chance of survival.

3. Higher fertility – an increase in the number of healthy calves or kids born per 100 females.

4. Level of damage – in locations where damage control is a major objective, damage level may have a controlling influence on the cull; damage monitoring must, therefore, be of high importance.

(Record keeping is more fully discussed in Chapter 2.5.)

Another aspect of cull planning is the time scale.

In Britain, there is a tendency to execute the bulk of the buck and stag cull before the rut for culinary reasons. Many consumers do not like the venison of beasts shot during the rut, which is strong in taste and aroma. It is a prudent stalker however who keeps a beast or two in hand in case an unwanted one, having eluded the early cull, suddenly appears and needs shooting.

It is also prudent to execute the bulk of the female cull early in the season before adverse weather causes loss of carcass weight. Here, delays are sometimes caused by the diversion of resources to other duties such as bird shooting from late October or November. There is a need perhaps for the distribution of resources so that one arm does not suffer in order to give strength to the other.

Finally, it has to be recognised that the planning must be linked to the objectives to be achieved. To this end, we will start with the logical approach to planning through the use of the Hoffman Pyramid method. This is followed by Planning Examples (pages 124-125), consideration of deer quality and planning adjustments which may be needed from time to time to either rationalise the structure of the population, to accommodate a change in management policies, or a change in the structure of the habitat.

In Figures 47-52 of the Culling chapter are the notes on Selection and Recognition (Pages 143-148).

Hoffman Pyramid

This section explains the construction and basic application of the Hoffman Pyramid approach. The example used is based on a holding of about 100 roe deer as an acceptable population (in the illustration each square equals *two* animals; the population is at sex parity, with the kid-production rate at the spring count of 100% of the does.

* * *

The Hoffman Pyramid is a logical method of visual presentation of deer population by age and sex, illustrating the need for a defined level of rational cull distributed between the sexes and through the age groups.

Many people find the Hoffman Pyramid in its 'original theoretical' form (steps 4-6 below), over-exact and therefore forbidding. Indeed it calls for a level of accuracy in ageing and recognising live deer which is almost unachievable. The 'conversion', however to the practical, 'blocked' format is more acceptable and perhaps even more persuasive.

The approach emphasises that:

1. There is always a significant surplus of calves/kids in relation to a defined size of deer population regardless of species of deer we are managing; this surplus *must* be culled. There is a school of thought which maintains, that for the sake of the return from venison, calves/kids should not be culled but left until they are a year old. This thinking must accept the consequent increase of pressure on the feeding platform (and damage). It also imposes an additional culling problem for it is usually easier to cull calves/kids with their mothers – as opposed to culling them as more independent yearlings. It also creates a younger age profile in the population. There is another reason for culling calves/kids; male yearlings may only be culled during the stag/buck season, male calves however, may be culled during the hind season provided the mothers are culled first.

2. The female side of the pyramid is more 'classical' in its form, showing a gradual reduction of the number of females with the increase in age, while the male side highlights the fact that the need to cull selectively should be concentrated on the younger beasts, leaving the middle and older males until they are ready for culling as a 'harvest' of high quality stags or bucks. The latter approach comes out particularly forcibly in the 'realistic' pyramid and less so in the purely theoretical one.

3. The top of the male (buck and stag) side of the pyramid is the reflection of the 'trophy harvest' which should aim at producing at least between 4% and 6% of the male population in a good supportive habitat in the 'full-age' structure.

4. There is another approach to the 'trophy harvest' – 'The Early Trophy Harvest' where bucks/stags are culled for trophies at the age when the development process of the antlers has reached a good 'trophy-worthy stage' (in terms of length, number of tines, palmation in fallow, pearling in roe, etc.). It accepts culling, therefore, before the full potential of development has been reached, in exchange for an earlier cull and a higher number of 'cullable' harvest heads.

Note:

The concept of 'Early Trophy Harvest' is very similar to felling trees in large numbers before full maturity, rather than waiting for full growth, thinning for space, and felling fewer but bigger trees at full maturity.

Fig.35   HOFFMAN PYRAMID IN EIGHT STEPS

1. Establish the average life span of deer in the locality ('A' = age)

2. Establish the population of deer as appropriate to your ground ('P' = population)

3. Draw a triangle with 'A' height, 'P' area (using graph paper). Area of Triangle P = (A x N) ÷ 2. ('N'= Numbers and is the base). Therefore by transposition N = 2P ÷ A. Recognise that sex ratio needs to be 1:1 giving ½N buck, ½N does, therefore, the triangle is in two halves.

Fig.35a

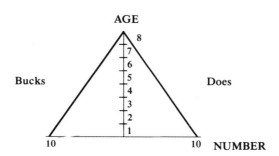

4. Calculate the number of young born each year, from the local spring calving rate. Divide then into 50/50 male and female and draw them in under the triangle (here the rate is 100% of does). Note you have many more kids than you need.

Fig.35b

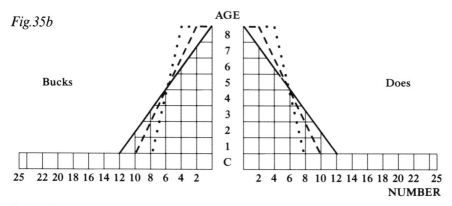

5. Decide the practical harvest level (see text), open up the top of the triangle, and reduce the bottom by an equal number to retain area. Shape now is trapezoid. (see text for limitations).

6. Convert the straight-line sides of the trapezoid which 'cuts' your beasts, into yearly steps. This shows how many beasts of each age you should have.

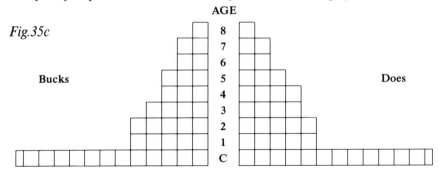

Fig.35c

7. Block in 4 age groups in rectangles: calves/kids, young, mature and old. Note the excess of kids/calves. This is the first step of 'the practical pyramid'.

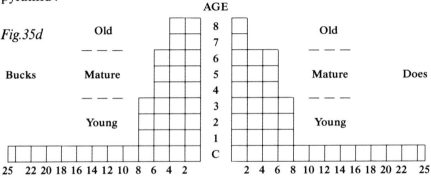

Fig.35d

8a. Copy and shade or colour the figure (at 7) above. It represents the next year's population. Overlay this on the previous year but 'one year' lower (as in the 'bucks' figure).

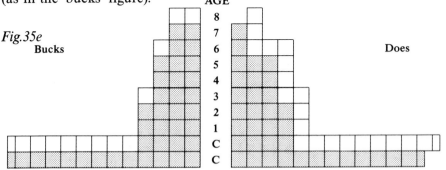

Fig.35e

The unshaded squares are your cull for the year. If you need to reduce your population but retain proportions, move the shaded pyramid by one 'beast' to the right (males) or left (females), (as in the 'does' figures).

8b. <u>*Early Trophy*</u> – Set the harvest at say 5 years, distribute 7 squares representing the ages 6, 7 and 8 years to young and mature blocks. Top line of mature block is the 'Early Trophy Harvest'.

Fig.35f

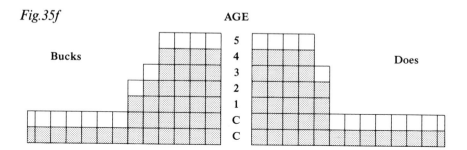

Quality in Deer

There is not much point in running a business enterprise without considering what quality of product or service the enterprise is providing. We monitor our output in terms of quality and strive for improvement. And yet in deer circles people shy away from the word 'quality' as applied to deer. This does not prevent some authors from writing articles about the deer shot during the year, primarily the best stags and bucks. They may say they are not writing about quality, but they carefully select in their review the dozen or two or even three of the best heads and write about these, giving measurements and other details. There is not a word about the other deer, culled in their thousands. So a quality selection has been carried out by the author and the best of the bunch described. But is it justifiable to take the best of the bunch out of the habitat?

The reviewers give the antler data, location and name of the 'rifle'. We do not, however, know very much more; the age of the beast – maybe it was too young to take out and should have been left, we don't know the weight, nor the total number of deer culled on each of the 'trophy' estates, and therefore what percentage the 'quality' represents. Was the one described a run-of-the-mill animal for a location proud of its quality, or was it an exception?

It could be that those who shy away from 'quality' talk when discussing deer know that quality cannot be applied universally. There are tremendous differences between the 'quality' of deer from various parts of the country, and indeed from different estates. These differences may have something to do with genetics, a lot to do with the quality of life the deer lead (food, shelter, numbers, sex ratio, all of which have a prime bearing), and a lot to do with the success of selective culling practised by the estate.

In describing the species we mentioned for instance the vast differences between Scottish Highland deer and Lowland forest deer. No way could one regard one lot as 'better quality' than the other. We could liken this to the quality of private transport we intend to provide. All right take the hackneyed comparison between your Ford and a Rolls Royce, but it goes deeper than that. Not only might you say that a Rolls is a 'better' car than a Ford, each within the parameters of their production objectives, but also it could be that, in the terrain where the transport is to be used, only horses, donkeys or camels are the appropriate and practical mode of transport. The Rolls or Ford are not in contention. Exactly the same applies to deer; a lowland woodland red deer is 'better', bigger in antlers and body, and can be compared only with its peers which have a similar quality of life. The thrust of deer management to 'improve quality' is therefore a local one, designed to improve the antlers, weight, calving rate, and survival by rationalising the population structure; providing deer with more and better food (without artificial feeding), and by ensuring that the food they forage for is of as good a nourishment value as can be practically provided.

The culling selection criteria presented in the following chapter have to be applied therefore against the local 'standard' otherwise, in a location where only a few, if any, roe deer develop a six-pointer head, most bucks would have to be culled out because they are not 'good enough'.

In talking of deer economics in Part 3 much emphasis is given to optimising income from deer. Better antlers give better stalking fees and better trophy fees, heavier bodies give more venison, all enhancing the sales value of our 'product'.

In Appendix E the reader will find the Conseil International de la Chasse (CIC) trophy measuring formulae. It is easy to see from these, what are the important 'quality' characteristics of the trophy. But, make no mistake, there are only a few deer that make CIC class – or to put it another, better way, of all the many thousands of deer culled every year only a minute percentage find themselves in the CIC class. This does not mean that only a few are top quality. It means that there are only a few medal winners. Medal winners? Yes – the same as in every sport, every show and competition, there are a few medal winners in the top class but the top class is quality class. This does not prevent millions from participating and enjoying the competition and making a useful contribution to the economy, sport, leisure, national health or prestige.

Nor, as had already been pointed out, is the 'trophy' the all important criterion so let us not translate the quality of deer into quality of antler, foresaking all others – let us remember the complete picture in which habitat plays a major role!

Adjustment of Population Structure

There are occasions when the policy of the owners or changes in the structure of environment, like change in the structure of forest or changes in the population of the range (such as new colonisation or migration) may call for a new and different approach to cull planning.

There is not a greater radical change than that which the Forestry Commission introduced into their attitude to deer, deer damage and deer control in mid 1960s. It may serve as an example.

* * *

Within the Forestry Commission, in its capacity both as a huge land-owner and as national policy advisor, co-ordinator and controller, much has changed in attitude to deer. Indeed much effort has been directed to addressing the many problems of deer management. Methodology, such as population estimates, forest landscaping, establishment of mixed forests and widening espacements in tree planting has been introduced. The general attitude towards deer and deer stalking among the Commission employees has vastly changed since the 1950s when deer were seen by many as vermin. Some of these facets of change present original new thinking, others are a development of ideas which, whilst not originating from the Commission, have been developed, adjusted and adopted by them.

Conscious of the dangers of deer damage, the Commission has blazed the trail of recognition that in different structural groups there are different deer damage problems because different tree-species/age profiles present different damage vulnerability. Indeed the Commission in its publications emphasises that, for instance, in sampling deer population, samples have to be applied only to the structural groups corresponding to those in which they have been taken. Surprisingly however, no indication has been given of what density of deer can be tolerated in different structural groups; in other words what is the level of acceptable *deer capacity* in different structural groups?

The level of tolerance of deer damage in commercial forests is that level at which the value of deer damage can be balanced by the value of revenue from deer. However, sensitivity towards damage by different owners, or perhaps 'friendliness' towards deer may dictate different levels of tolerance and therefore different deer capacities in similar structural groups. The Commission is a good example of this for in the earlier days their tolerance of deer damage level was near zero since they hoped to exterminate deer. This approach has drastically changed in that, whilst not quantified (or at least not published), the Commission accepts a degree of reasonable damage and recognises deer as an inevitable inhabitant of woodlands.

That deer will do damage to most woodlands goes without saying. Whilst there is a correlation between the level of deer damage and deer density, there is also no doubt that it is not a direct, straight line correlation and that cutting deer density by half will not reduce deer damage by half. The simplest explanation of this phenomenon is that in reducing deer density fewer deer remain to feed on the total food available, and within that total feeding resource much food can be consumed without resorting to damaging the valuable trees. Alas, however, residual tree damage will be always suffered because trees do represent an attractive feed, especially certain tree species at certain ages (usually young) and at certain times of the year (when food is otherwise scarce).

Maybe, one would have expected the Forestry Commission to direct more of their research resources to the issue of damage potential to different tree species, at different ages, related to different deer density levels, thus providing a 'density scale' which could be applied to management of deer in a forest. If such research is under way no indication of the results has been made public.

The effort needed to rationalise deer population structures, scaled up to the size of land ownership such as the Forestry Commission's would be vast and could be applied only gradually. Whilst accepting the ultimate need for such rationalisation, priority has to rest in a numerical control of deer to reduce the risk of damage, but within the parameters of preservation and commercial exploitation of deer as an asset.

Deer are a source of significant revenue to the Commission as a result of the changed policy.

* * *

Another policy change comes from the MacAuley Land Use Research Institute. The Institute has been experimenting with hill deer for 20 or so years but its main thrust has been agricultural land use. We now hear that they are about to run experimental trials of their new computer programme whereby they will be able to provide deer capacity levels for the Scottish hills, based on the vegetation and geophysical profile of different locations. This programme is an extension of their programme which was developed years ago for hill sheep. Thus for the first time there will be data upon which it will be possible to quantify the over-population of red deer on the hill, relating it to a specific locality. This is a most important matter because so far, all 'directives' and 'proposals' relating to deer population levels, whether issued by the Nature Conservancy Council, Red Deer Commission, or Scottish Landowners' Federation, were dubious, lacking any credible quantification.

* * *

These examples may have been a diversion, but they reinforce the notion that adjustment of the population is necessary from time to time and that those responsible for deer management must be ready to apply it.

Situations of planned increase in deer population are so rare that we can discard them, with one exception. Where changes to the structure of the forest occur and the vulnerability of trees to damage has decreased it may be acceptable to allow the population to increase. Assuming that the population has been rationalised in terms of age and sex structure, the increase is usually allowed through decreasing the yearly cull of all age bands, except the oldest where a decrease in culling may increase the age mortality.

The most frequent situation is to move from an almost unmanaged population to a rationalised one. The unmanaged population is usually one where there is a surfeit of young deer because calves or kids are unculled, and a surplus of females because any culling that has been done is that of bucks and stags. This calls for a heavy cull, in the first place of the calves or kids and of females, as well as a high cull of both sexes at the low age band. In a managed population at a sex ratio of about 1 : 1, the excess of calves and kids which has to be culled is at least 20% of red deer calves and about 50% (and sometimes more) of roe kids (see Hoffman Pyramid, page 117). It stands to reason that if the females exceed males by a factor of three, three times more young are produced and the cull must be increased by the same or greater factor.

The young class may also need a heavy cull initially, but as the recruitment of calves or kids decreases as a result of heavy culling, so gradually the cull of the young class may be allowed to decrease.

One of the difficulties in a large scale reduction cull is the practicality of handling it with the resources available. We should not try to reduce the numbers too rapidly; it must be accepted that reduction is a long process, not only because there are limits to what the available stalkers can cull in a year, but also how much venison can be marketed (no one likes having to bury culled beasts). The real problem, however, lies in the fact that the family structure, behaviour and physiology of the animals tends to be gravely and adversely affected if the cull exceeds 30% of the local population of either sex. This may seem an unlikely cull in real situations and yet it can happen if deer have been forced to migrate and settle in a new location which cannot bear the increase.

Annex to Chapter 2.3.

Deer Population Planning Examples

Example 1 - (Fig.36a)

The figures alongside represent the current deer population. The population is to be reduced to 100 adult beasts, with a rationalised age.

Alongside (A) is the pyramid of the present and required deer population (shading reflects the cull needed) which is by far too extensive to be attempted in one year.

Age	Buck	Does
8	0	0
7	0	7
6	2	10
5	10	16
4	15	25
3	35	30
2	40	35
1	40	40
Adults	142	163
Kids	65	65
Total	207	228

Alongside (B) is the pyramid of the target structure with the yearly cull shaded.

Example 2 - (Fig.36b)

Alongside is a graph showing red deer population over 18 years and the levels of total and hind cull during that time.

This is a clear indication how an inadequate hind cull and a high total cull (therefore stags and calves) allows the population to grow.

Fig.36a   CULL PLANNING EXAMPLES

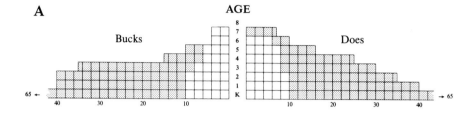

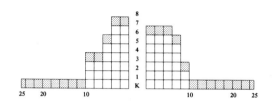

□ each square = 2 roe deer

Fig.36b

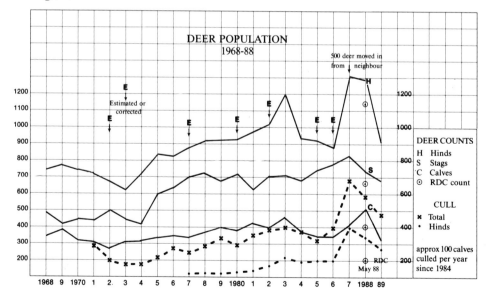

2.4. Culling

WHEN DEER are managed as a constituent part of a larger operation like forestry or farming, their control must be kept in its correct perspective. We can afford to put deer on a pedestal as a splendid, interesting and sporting animal and manage it within its habitat to optimise its beauty, quality, sporting interest or scientific research value. When deer are managed as a product, because they have to be recognised as such under the prevailing economic conditions, their control becomes a sensitive and important consideration; the others, however important, must take second place.

Within the overall concept of numerical control we may bring in considerations of selection and rationalisation of age and sex structure. These become important not only because they are good for the deer but because by this rationalisation the financial return from deer can be optimised through improvement of quality whilst damage is kept to an acceptably low level. These issues will be further discussed in Part 3 – here we need to address the question of methods to be adopted when and if we conduct the cull – with regard to selection of quality, selection to adjust the age structure and selection to rationalise the sex structure.

Culling must be recognised as an activity which has two different purposes. Firstly, to control the numbers of deer, meaning the reduction of numbers, adjusting the age and/or sex structure and the subsequent maintenance of the population. Reduction of numbers is usually linked to reaching an acceptable level of damage. These objectives must be paramount; numerical reduction to an acceptable level related to the incidence of damage.

The second purpose, which in the later stages may be included in the first, is the harvest of deer as a product of the forest. But 'harvest' means the cull of mature 'trophy-worthy' and therefore fee-attracting stags or bucks. Undeniably, in the control of numbers operation there is an element of 'harvest': venison can be sold and stalking can be let, thus creating income. But the objectives remain different, and to achieve the second, the development of quality trophies is an essential consideration.

Sometimes the culling of male deer gets off on the wrong foot because those responsible for deer policy, forest management and deer management do not adequately understand deer. Being intent on the protection of trees when they see a powerful master buck or stag creating wanton damage in tree standings by fraying they cull the culprit. The result they do not foresee is that in the place of one damage maker, who probably returned more or less to the same trees and re-marked them several times, in come several other younger contenders, each satisfied with a lesser territory or smaller hind herd and each needing to establish himself and marking his boundaries on different trees.

Culling for numerical control of deer has three basic planning stages:

1. Initial and then periodic estimation and monitoring of the numbers of deer.
2. Analysis of the forest by its structure (species and ages) in identifiable blocks, followed by a decision on an acceptable damage related density (capacity) level, for each structural block.
3. Planning and execution of the cull based on 1 and 2 above.

Note:

In application to the small deer, muntjac and Chinese water deer numerical control is the only consideration, the concepts of density and capacity (below) do not come into play, because counting these deer is just about impossible. Although culling techniques are not discussed in this work a few words about muntjac cull may be useful. Prior[20] quotes a forester who induces muntjac to follow a 'track' opened-up by dragging a tree trunk through thick undergrowth. This could be compared with the Continental method of still-hunting (sitting up) for foxes in thick cover. A line of wire mesh is staked in thick cover parallel and close to the edge of an artificially made track (as above) inducing the quarry to follow the track over which the 'hunter' waits. The mesh could even be the same as used for flushing pheasants!

Density and Capacity

Density and capacity are concepts which are not always understood – they come up in this book over and over again. It is essential that they be understood fully and therefore an earlier chapter has been devoted to the theme. Without this understanding the problems discussed in the chapters which follow will not fall into their right perspective.

Cull Size

Cull size is a function of density and population dynamics. At the initial stage of management of deer in symbiosis with the forest, density may be too high, perhaps because they have not been managed and controlled

[20] Prior, R., *Shooting Times* (September 1991).

adequately. If so, a high cull will be required until the desired, acceptable level of density is reached.

In an overstocked forest the cull of female deer must be given high priority. Forest female deer living in a supportive habitat have high fertility rates and their calves/kids high survival rates; there are reports of roe doe being seen feeding three or even four kids and red deer hinds feeding twins. Just as triplets (or quads) are unusual in roe so twins are unusual in red deer. Red deer 'twins' are most probably the hind's own calf plus an orphaned calf of another hind. All the same, very high calving and survival rates in a good, deer-friendly, woodland environment is a fact, and must be reflected in high culling rates to contain the population. At the same time, it must be remembered that culls in excess of 30% of the adult population of either sex within the range, and within one season produce excessive stress in deer, disrupting the social structure, and may therefore be detrimental to their health and behaviour. In a large scale population decrease it is necessary to spread the increased culls over several years.

Hind/Doe Undercull

The effect of a hind or doe undercull is usually misinterpreted. All too frequently one shrugs it off and suggests "we will cull an extra one next year or sometime". Next year never comes, because it is not just 'one' next year, but 2, and it is more like 10 in five years time, as the diagram below shows.

If it is 10 in year 5 with red deer, where calves are not born to year old hinds, and born only in singles, how much worse it is with roe deer where a one-year old can produce twins and where triplets are not uncommon!

Fig.37 HIND UNDERCULL

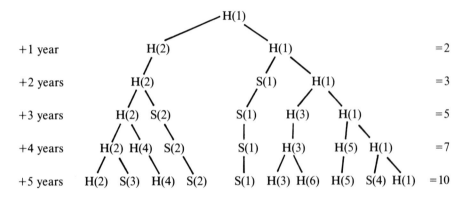

128

Fig.38   ROE DOE UNDERCULL

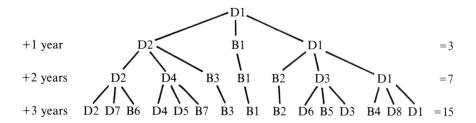

+1 year	D2		B1		D1		=3
+2 years	D2 D4	B3 B1	B2	D3		D1	=7
+3 years	D2 D7 B6	D4 D5 B7	B3 B1	B2	D6 B5 D3	B4 D8 D1	=15

It is obvious, and yet insufficiently practiced, that the level of culling and the level of natural increase need to be related to each other; that when reduction of population is the target, the cull has to exceed, often significantly, the level of natural increase. When it is intended to maintain the *status quo*, the level of cull must about equal that of the natural increase; allowance being made not only for the cull level but also mortality due to other natural or unnatural causes ('natural increase' meaning in reality the rate of first-winter-survival and not the birth rate). In the cull, quality of deer is an important consideration, and selection principles should be followed whenever possible (qualitative selection is discussed later in this chapter).

To help in cull planning a simple model, shown below, can be used (the following model applies to red deer – note the calving rate; in roe deer the fawning rate would be double the figure or even higher).

Fig.39   CULL PLAN MODEL - HINDS

Number of hinds	100	less culled	13 =	87
Number of calves* at				
40% calving 50/50 m/f (here female)	20	less culled	2 =	+ 18
Mortality (say 2%)		less deaths		− 2
Total left to next year				103

(therefore the number is growing slightly)

Number of hinds	100	less culled	25 =	75
Number of calves* at				
40% calving 50/50 m/f (here female)	20	less culled	2 =	+ 18
Mortality (say 2%)		less deaths		− 2
Total left to next year				91

(therefore the number is decreasing)

* To avoid any confusion; 100 hinds at 40% calving rate (March count) = 40 calves, at 50/50 sex ratio 20 male and 20 female calves.

In culling for numerical reduction and protection against damage, males should not be neglected. Not only do they need to eat, they create damage, and also good management principles require us to gear the sex ratio to about 1:1 as explained in Chapter 2.3.

It may also be necessary to consider the mix of deer species, not on account of their influence upon the forest through damage but their inter-species co-existence. Some deer do not thrive in the company of others. For instance roe deer will live with red, but will rarely produce good quality and fallow can be physically hostile to roe deer. A species culling policy may also be needed to prevent possible hybridisation as with red/sika.

Calves and Kids

It is suggested in this book as well as several others that it is important to include in the annual cull a significant number of calves/kids and yearlings.

There is much opposition mainly on two possible grounds:

1. People do not like shooting the young;
2. 'We might be culling a future trophy buck or stag'.

Because of the latter the cull of young males is delayed until the antlers show signs of quality, which is about the fourth year in the large deer and the third year in roe.

One has to understand both sentiments but it is important at the same time to understand the logic of culling young deer. Not only does the logic of age structure demand it (see the Hoffman Pyramid), but also by preserving the young we are maintaining unnecessarily high grazing pressure on the habitat.

Take an example: an area where two hundred (200) deer are to be held at the sex ratio of 1:1; therefore 100 male and 100 female. Take the 'no youngster cull' syndrome and apply it to red and roe deer to see the effects. The model below assumes that the calving rate of red deer (March count) is 40% and roe deer 80% (*Fig.40*).

By the time culling of young animals is allowed under this regime the population of 200 consists of 42.5% deer aged three years and lower, with 53 stags aged over three years to build up an age structure between the ages of four and fifteen.

Roe Deer

It is easy to visualise how much worse would be the case of roe deer where calving could be double or more that of red deer. The same exercise set with roe deer, with a recruitment rate of only 80% would produce after *only two years* – 39 bucks, 40 does (adult) and 121 two years old and younger, of which 79 are yearlings and older (50% females of kid-bearing age).

The calf and kid cull is usually linked to the hind and doe cull. Many maintain that whenever possible, when culling a female, the young is also culled. Cull figures prove this sentiment is not executed. If we accept calving as being (say) in the region of 40% of the females, a cull of 100 females should produce something approaching 40 calves. In practice it hardly ever does. On average in most locations where calves or kids are culled the total cull rarely exceeds 20% of the females. If nothing else it is cruel to cull the mother and leave the young; that is why the Cruelty to Animals Act allows male calves to be culled during the stag/buck close season.

Fig.40

ADVERSE EFFECTS OF 'NO CULLING UNDER 3 YEARS' ON THE ADULT POPULATION

Red Deer	Stags	Hinds	Calves		Total		Cull to maintain total
				old	young		
Year 1							
Adult population	100	100		200			
100 hinds @ 40% produce 40 calves			40		40		
No young culled mortality 5%			−2		−2		
	100	100	38	200	38		−38 50/50M/F
Cull	−19	−19					
State	81	81	38	162	38		
Year 2							
81 hinds @ 40% produce 32 calves			32		32		
Calves from Year 1					38		
No young culled mortality 5%			−4(28)		−4		
	81	81		162	66		−28 50/50M/F
Cull	−14	−14					
State	67	67		134	66		
Year 3							
67 old hinds @ 40% +19 young hinds ex yr 1		+19					
produce 34 calves			34		34		
Calves from yr 1 & 2					66(−19)		
No young culled mortality 5%			−5(29)		−5		
	67	86			76		−29 50/50M/F
Cull	−14	−15					
State	53	71		124	76		

Finer Points of Selection

Quality Through Selective Cull

There are those who, not believing that heredity and genetic influence play a role, discard selection as having an influence on quality. Some of them may even be scientists but, whoever they are, they are not looking practical facts in the face.

Selective culling has several objectives, the first of which is the elimination of those beasts which are obviously sick or below the local 'standard'. Whether or not they are old animals, very good bucks or stags (it does no-one any good to find dead deer with gold medal heads which have perished in a ditch or bog because of ill-health), beasts with badly formed heads or females which are known to be regularly barren need to be taken out on welfare grounds as well as for the benefit of the owner. Heredity should not even be considered in these circumstances, but there is an added benefit in taking out such animals if heredity was responsible for the disease or other disorder which caused the animal to be below standard in the first place (I believe that heredity does play an important role in quality propagation).

Rationalisation of age and sex structure is an integral part of selection for quality. The cull should therefore cover all age groups in such a manner that the remaining stock is at a logically predetermined and rational age and sex structure as previously explained and illustrated by the Hoffman Pyramid.

There is a prerequisite to selective culling that needs to be hammered home – even people who see deer frequently neglect to pay sufficient attention to body shape, from which age can be approximately determined. Body shape characteristics change with age throughout the life span of most, if not all, deer species and recognition of body shape at any particular stage in an animal's life span can provide a rough guide to its age (see *Fig.2* pages 16 & 17).

Why is this so important? Firstly, this is one of the few criteria we have for ageing females in the field. Secondly, ageing a male deer by antler growth and shape can be very misleading, but we are so attracted by the antlers that we tend to do so, neglecting other confirmatory criteria. Antlers develop differently according to location and what is a good antler in one part of the country may be classified as poor elsewhere. Judging age by antler appearance alone, without reference to other criteria such as body shape, can thus be a costly mistake.

Earlier, in the chapters devoted to descriptions of the various species, the timing of antler shedding and cleaning and pelage change were discussed. These are useful indications of age, but a great degree of accuracy should not be expected. They are summarised in the Annex to this chapter.

Red Deer

A three year old stag on the hill or in the woodland is about fully developed in his body and thus comparable in size with his elders, but his neck is thinner than that of a fully mature stag, because from the age of four they start growing a mane which adds thickness to the neck. It is not until the three year old starts to grow its winter coat that the neck starts 'filling' on the underside, not with flesh but with the beginning of the mane. The telling characteristics are the straight line of the back from the shoulders and the head carried high with a protruding long, comparatively thin nose/jaw line.

With advancing age the face loses its slimness and starts filling, the pointed muzzle becomes blunter and therefore looks shorter. The same applies to the neck but it is not only the mane which gives the neck its thickness, it is also the flesh. Slowly the neck becomes fuller each year until the old beast looks thick-set at the neck, with a pouch of the underneck adding thickness. In comparison, the females lose neck flesh with advancing age.

The shoulders which at the age of about four formed a straight line from the rump to the base of the neck start protruding at about the fifth or sixth year. By the age of eight or nine the neck breaks above the shoulder, falling down from there both back towards the rump and to the base of the neck. This characteristic is not so pronounced in hinds.

We said that the young stag's head is held high, the neck curving like a waning moon with the head at the top. With age the curve fills up hence the erectness of the head becomes less pronounced; at the same time the head is held lower with advancing age so that the back line of an old undisturbed stag runs in a straight line from behind the ears to a point in front of the shoulder, and then drops down from behind the shoulder to the rump. By this time the stag's mane is rich and long and makes the neck look very deep and short.

In addition to body shape there is the position in which the head is carried. A young stag when walking or even running carries his head high, the angle of the nose bone being probably about 30 degrees below horizontal. As the stag ages, so the head is held lower. This may be minimal in the first few years, but at a later stage it becomes more noticeable, ending at old age with the shoulder becoming the high body point and muzzle pointing groundwards. However, these characteristics are hardly discernible if the animal is startled or alerted and takes to flight. In some countries there is an apt description of the appearance of an old stag either coming straight at you or going away: 'He looks as if antlers are growing from his stomach'.

Fallow Deer

The differences between a fallow fully developed in body at say three years and an old one is much less distinct than in red deer. Fawns do have a 'Bambi' appearance for a while but it is not as exaggerated as in red and roe, perhaps because the neck remains very thin only for a matter of a few weeks. Hence one of the best indications of young age is denied us. Until the animal is about two years old the face has a pointed appearance with a small muzzle, deep from the forehead to the back of the jaw; this feature starts disappearing at about the third or fourth year as the muzzle thickens. The neck does thicken with age but not as much as in red deer, nor is the position of the head as good or as clear an indication of age. Fallow tend to be alert and on the lookout more than the other deer and the head held at the high 'alert' position. It is the antlers that we have to rely on more in this species.

Sika Deer

In general terms the descriptions for red deer are applicable to sika. The shape of the head however, can be misleading because the sika's face is blunter and its colouration makes the head appear very different to what it really is.

Roe Deer

The roe fawn ('kid' the correct term but 'fawn' is more appealing) is more the 'Disney Bambi' than the young of the other species. Maybe it is its size, with large almost white spots, very large black eyes and enormous ears (in relation to the size of face), with foreshortened body and very long spindly and knock-kneed legs, that make the roe kid look like Bambi. Even on entering the second year of life roe still look baby-like; the body may be larger and starts filling, the legs are more proportionate to the body but the neck is still very thin and the ears large for the size of the head. This characteristic is emphasized by the inquisitive alert posture that a young roe deer always holds.

Having said that we must remember that a roe doe is fully developed by the time she is 13 months old, is often fertilised and drops her first young just after her second birthday, hence in terms of body build roe mature quicker than the larger deer. By the time they reach their first birthday the neck no longer has the ridiculously elongated willow-like appearance and starts filling.

From the age of five the head starts being carried lower every year; we must remember that a five year old buck has reached maturity and probably maximum antler development. He is within a year of being regarded as old. An old buck has a thick neck which appears short, his head is carried low, so low that in the last year or two of his life the nose bone is at right angles to the ground. The doe, being on the look-out, always holds her head erect whatever her age.

We need to remember that roe deer are almost as alert as fallow and the slightest suspicion of danger will send the head up.

Antlers

In each of the different species of deer antlers grow in different shapes and sizes, but there are some inter-species similarities e.g. in red and sika deer now resident on the European Continent and in the open range antlers are generally similar and as far as we know, much of what is said about red deer antlers also applies to sika. Red deer and sika have of course hybridised in Scotland and the Irish Republic, but so far not yet in the New Forest-Dorset area.

There are however, significant differences in antler size and shape between individuals of each species. Some of the differences are regional, some may be a matter of heredity and some are due to habitat differences, primarily the availability of food and shelter. Abnormalities occasioned by mechanical injury or misfunction of internal organs in an individual can also influence, temporarily or permanently, antler symmetry, shape and size. Many temporary malformations are due to damage to antlers during their growth, whilst damage to the pedicle usually has a lasting effect.

It must also be remembered that the basic shape of antler in a given animal is retained from year to year after the age of about three years. The number of tines may increase in the early years and decrease as the antler 'goes back' in late life, the same applies to length but the general shape remains provided that the animal is healthy and has adequate food. It is often forgotten that the antler shape of first and second heads is not necessarily a foretaste of what the adult antler will be like. Thus an ugly looking antler with 'kinks' and 'bends' is not necessarily a bad one, for each kink and bend is probably a promise of future tines.

Red Deer

The development of antlers should, more or less, follow the outline below:

1st head : Should be as long as the ears or longer; may have small tines; 'kinks' suggest location of tines in the future.
2nd head : Should have small brows or top fork, but very long tineless antler is acceptable especially with kinks.
3rd head : Should be a six pointer or better.
4th head : Must be at least six pointer good quality would be eight points and more; beam starts thickening with weight in the upper beam at or below the top fork.
5th head : Has the full complement of tines, but head still grows longer and beam thicker.

6-8th heads : Antlers fully developed, brows may start drooping towards the limit of age class.

Old : Tines become blunt, lose length, thickness of the beam drops to lower beam.

Fig.41   RED DEER – ANTLER DEVELOPMENT

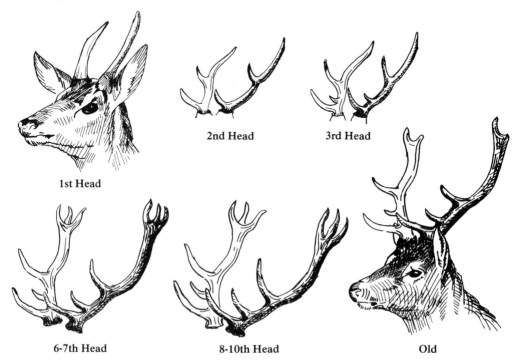

1st Head

2nd Head

3rd Head

6-7th Head

8-10th Head

Old

We are concerned here with selection as an aid to quality and red deer (and only marginally sika), have one very important antler characteristic which is infallible from the third head onwards.

Fig.42 RED DEER – TRIANGLE/RECTANGLE PRINCIPLE

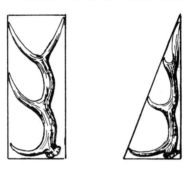

An antler, which in profile can be inscribed into a triangle is poor and has no development potential, whereas one that needs a rectangle is the one with a good future.

Fallow Deer

Fallow deer of trophy quality must develop palmation; there are herds where palmations are rare or non-existent. One could compare this to herds of red deer where royals never develop and could be attributed to heredity or poor feeding.

Palmation in a well developed fallow should be about half of the total antler length and the width about half of the palmation length.

The general outline of antler development also follows a pattern:

1st head : Should be the length of the ears and of a uniform thickness; tines are exceptional.

2nd head : Should have a brow and at least one other tine; palmation may start developing in the top of the beam, showing as a flat 'spoon'.

3rd head : Must have brow and bey fully developed with palmation showing, spreading upwards and fore-and-aft, the rear edge may show small knobs of future tines (spellers) but the spur and top-fore should be larger.

4th head : Is a development of the third with tines growing longer; the palmation should be solid.

5th & later : The palmation develops thicker, the depressions between the spellers may grow deeper in later years suggesting the head has started going back. Maximum development usually happens in about the seventh or eighth head.

Fig.43   FALLOW DEER – ANTLER DEVELOPMENT

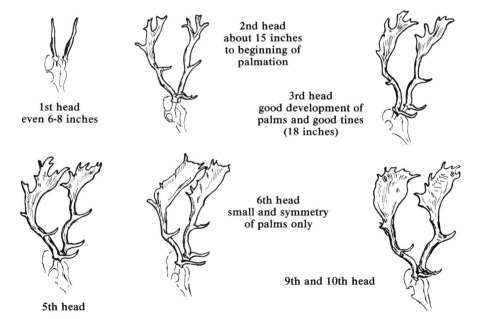

1st head
even 6-8 inches

2nd head
about 15 inches
to beginning of
palmation

3rd head
good development of
palms and good tines
(18 inches)

5th head

6th head
small and symmetry
of palms only

9th and 10th head

Sika Deer

The sika antler is of a simpler structure than that of red deer and the triangle/rectangle rule does not apply to it for most antlers grow to a triangular shape. The quality is in the length of the tines and thickness as well as length of the beam. First and second head are very much like those of a red deer. By the fourth head the full number of tines (usually four aside but sometimes five) should be developed.

The sixth to ninth heads show little difference other than in thickness of the beam and tines. After that age there is a chance of going back.

Crowns are unknown in pure bred sika stags as are the bey tines.

Fig.44   SIKA DEER – ANTLER DEVELOPMENT

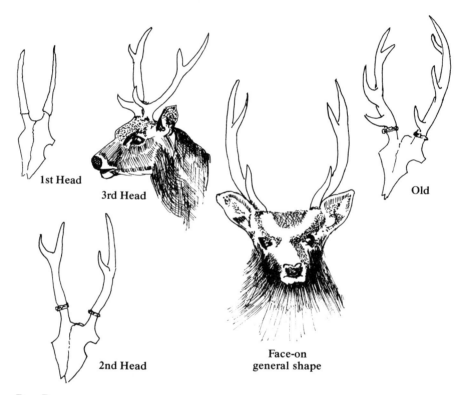

1st Head

3rd Head

Old

2nd Head

Face-on
general shape

Roe Deer

It is important to remember that roe deer, having a shorter life span than the larger deer, grow and develop more rapidly – the general pattern of development is as follows:

1st head   : Must be the length of ears, usually spiky, straight. If there are kinks they indicate future tines. Burrs and pearling are hardly visible.

2nd head   : Should be longer, but must have at least a top fork. The burrs and pearling should be well marked. Very thick and well pearled tineless head or one lacking tines but two-three inches longer than the ears are acceptable.

3rd head   : At this age the antlers should be a full six pointer. The burrs and pearling are fully developed with the antlers significantly longer than the ears.

4th & later : The antlers may grow marginally longer, but should become significantly thicker with larger burrs and strong pearling. All tines sharp.

Old   : At the age of six or thereabouts the antlers may start going back, tines get blunter and shorter but the antlers may grow thicker with thick drooping burrs.

Fig.45   ROE DEER – ANTLER DEVELOPMENT

Age and Sex Structure Selection

There are too many people who pooh-pooh the concept of rationalised age and sex structure until they start writing and complaining: too many hinds, not enough mature stags, and so on. These comments are almost exclusively addressed to red deer; not because they are unique but because it is among the highly visible hill deer where imbalances are easily spotted. They would also apply to many woodlands however, where woodland red deer and all other species usually reside. These exclamations indicate how important rationalisation of both sex and age structure is to deer management and how little it is properly understood. It does not mean that there is one yardstick which must be always applied – open range deer may need a different sex and age structure rationale than their park or farm brethren. But wherever they are and whatever their habitat, a rational and logical management policy must be applied to the age and sex structure.

It may be that many people do not know how to achieve this, they do not address the question and complain when it is too late. Others do not wish to commit the effort needed, and as always there are those who do not care.

The battle for a good sex and age structure starts at the calf/kid stage and goes on right through the life span and needs to be included in the selective cull.

Sex Structure

The start of rationalisation is at birth. In most, if not all, deer offspring are born at about sex parity. Early in life males are more vulnerable and a few more die than females; as a counter-balance, females do not live as long as males. Thus Nature provides the basic structure.

It is now generally accepted that the sex structure of deer in the open range should be maintained at the level of about 1 : 1. Not only are deer conceived and born at that ratio but it is also the ratio at which deer thrive in the natural state.

It is very interesting that world-wide research suggests that the ratio of 1 : 1 applies to all deer wherever they may live. Once however, the ratio is upset and is female dominated, the return to 1 : 1 or thereabouts is a slow and laborious process. It calls for a high cull of the females and their young (culls in the region of 25%-30% of adult females have been known), as shown in *Fig.46*.

Fig.46 AGE CULL ADJUSTMENT MODEL – ROE DEER
(Recruitment c 80%)

Age (up to):	1	2	3	4	5	6	7	8	Total
Year 1									
Bucks	30	15	3	3	–	–	–	–	51
cull	–	–	–	–	–	–	–	–	–
Does	50	19	20	26	32	34	–	–	181
cull	–	–	–	–	–	–	–	–	–
Year 2									
Bucks	50	30	15	3	3	–	–	–	101
cull	21	8	–	–	–	–	–	–	29
Does	52	50	19	20	26	32	34	–	233
cull	27	20	–	–	–	8	25	–	80
Year 3									
Bucks	51	29	22	15	3	3	–	–	123
cull	34	9	2	3	1	2	–	–	51
Does	51	25	30	19	20	26	24	9	204
cull	34	7	10	–	–	6	4	9	70
Year 4									
Bucks	47	17	20	20	12	2	1	–	119
cull	27	4	4	6	4	1	1	–	47
Does	47	17	18	20	19	20	20	20	181
cull	27	3	2	4	3	4	10	20	73
Year 5									
Bucks	35	20	13	16	14	8	1	–	107
cull	20	3	2	4	2	4	–	–	35
Does	35	20	14	16	16	16	16	10	143
cull	20	6	1	2	2	8	8	10	57
Year 6 (5th year of planned shooting)									
Bucks	28	15	17	11	12	12	4	1	100
cull	16	4	2	–	2	3	1	–	28
Does	28	15	14	13	14	14	8	8	114
cull	15	5	2	1	3	5	3	8	42
State of population after 6 years planned shooting:									
Bucks	12	11	15	11	10	9	3	1	72
Does	13	10	12	12	11	9	5	–	72

At this stage it would be fairly easy to build up the upper ages of buck to introduce a 'pyramid' shape as suggested elsewhere. The remaining 72 does would produce about 56 kids every year, i.e. about 28 of each sex.

Typical and central to this solution is the fact that it takes about one life span of the species in question before a rational age and sex structure is achieved; this would be with red deer about 14 to 16 years. During that time careful culling with the ability to estimate the age of live deer before shooting is essential. For this reason, the model above covers roe deer where results after six years are feasible.

Age and Age Structure

In managing deer in the open range, especially for stalking and trophy quality, it is essential that the deer population is so structured that the males reach the 'trophy worthy' or 'harvesting' age, whilst the female population is culled out at the age when kid/calf bearing and mothering qualities start to decline. In open range deer management for venison this form of structure is not important.

All too often it is not understood that if we want the age distribution to cover the life span where a deer population is maintained at a pre-determined level, culling of calves/kids/fawns is an essential prerequisite.

An imbalance of age structure, where there is a lack of mature and old beasts calls for high culls at the young end of the spectrum, culling calves/kids and yearlings of both sexes and conserving the maturing and mature beasts, except for those which on account of their quality or health are unwanted. This approach allows for the preservation and build-up of a stock of trophy quality animals. The age to which these beasts should be left unculled will differ not only with species but location. Certainly male animals should be culled as they reach the age of going back, female deer when their mothering production starts to decline.

I invite those who do not believe in the need to cull calves and yearlings heavily to study the model in *Fig.40* and develop their own theories.

Our aim must be to cull out a proportion of kids and yearlings in order to allow a part of the population to reach the age of eight when the bucks become trophy and fee-worthy producers. We would expect that 5-6% of the male population would be trophy worthy producers.

This principle can be applied to all deer allowing only for longevity and the locally accepted rate of natural increase.

SEASON RELATED GUIDE SUMMARY – RED DEER

Fig.47

		Jan.	Feb.	Mar.	Apr.	May.	Jun.	Jul.	Aug.	Sept.	Oct.	Nov.	Dec.
HINDS	0–1 year						Calves born		Coat loses spots grows brown-grey				
	2yr-mature				Coat changes to summer					Coat changes to winter brown		Tend to form family groups	
	Old					Coat changes to summer				Coat changes to winter			
STAGS	0–1 year			Knobs develop to spikes					First coat change			Male calves in hind herds	
	1–2 years					Casts spike / Coat change to summer				2 year old join stag groups	Clean velvet – Rut		
STAGS	3-Mature				Casts antler / Change to summer coat			Must be 8 pointers by age of 5 or 6 Prime heads by 9		Clean velvet – Rut	Clean velvet – Rut	Change to winter coat	
	Old 8 years		Casts antler / Change coat to summer					Clean velvet Can start going back from 9 or 10 yrs		Rut – change coat to winter			

Fig.48

CULL GUIDE SUMMARY – RED DEER

Age Band	Shootable	Non-shootable
YOUNG	a. Calves 4 – 7 months old are culled as part of the hind cull, the deciding factor being age and primarily the numbers to be culled. b. Yearlings – those with antlers shorter than ears, spikers – unless very thick antlered. c. Numerical cull of yearlings of both sexes take priority over quality. d. 2 year old – Spikers ear length or less unless antlers thin, without tines or promise of tines. e.	– Those with antlers longer than the ears, antlers with tines – brows or top fork. – Long antlers, tines formed e.g. brows and/or small top fork. – Exceptionally long, thick at upper beams.
MATURE 4–8 years	a. Short spiker head. b. 4-point and fewer at the bottom of the age group or less than 8 points at the upper group. c. From the fourth year those with "triangular" shape, and those below the local norm. *See also the "Triangle/Rectangle" method page 136*	– Six-pointer and better with fair length, and weight in upper antler. – Better than those shootable.
OLD 9 years and more.	a. Poorly developed, irregular or "ugly". b. Good quality heads showing signs of going back for two consecutive years. c. All stags of known age of 13 years and more; better culled than allowed to die.	– Well developed, with 8 and more points and with good weight at the upper antler.

Notes : 1. Numerical cull achievement and crop protection takes priority.
2. Quality must be assessed against the local "norm".
3. Captive deer and those fed can not be judged by the above criteria.

Fig.49

SEASON RELATED GUIDE SUMMARY – FALLOW DEER

	Jan.	Feb.	Mar.	Apr.	May.	Jun.	Jul.	Aug.	Sept.	Oct.	Nov.	Dec.
DOES — Fawns	Mixed herds until June						Fawns born	Coat loses spots grows winter colour			Rut	Tend to join family group mixed herds growing into first rut
Yearling				Coat changes to summer					Coat changes to winter			
2yrs–mature				Coat changes to summer					Coat changes to winter			
Old					Coat changes to summer					Coat changes to winter	Rut	
BUCKS — Fawns		Tufts of hair					Fawns born			Grows pedicle / Coat loses spots grows winter		
1–2 years	Mixed Herds until June			Casts spike	Grows spike / Coat change to summer / Casts first head				Cleans velvet / Cleans antler		1st Rut	
2yrs–mature				Coat change to summer / Casts antler / Coat change / Casts antler				Coat change to winter / Cleans antler / Coat change / Cleans antler (by 5th antler full palmation)	Cleans second head	Coat change to winter	Rut	Bucks in separate herds
8 years +			Cast antler / Can start going back at 9 years	Change coat to summer / Casts antler				Coat change to winter / Cleans antler			Rut	

Fig.50

CULL GUIDE SUMMARY – FALLOW DEER

Age Band	Shootable		Non-shootable
YOUNG Fawns–3 years	a.	Calves 4 - 7 months old are culled as part of the doe cull, the deciding factor is age and condition of mothers and above all the numbers to be culled.	
	b.	Yearlings – with short antlers (Numerical cull of fawns and yearlings takes priority over quality)	– Yearlings with antlers longer than the ears.
	c.	2yrs old spikers ear length and less, unless antlers are thick at the top and not showing signs of palmation.	– 2yrs old antlers longer than the ear, with brow tine or flattened at top starting palmation.
	d.	3yrs old – as above.	– Starting palmation and good brown tine.
MATURE 4–8 years	a.	Tineless and palmless antler.	– Palmated heads with good brow developing spellers off the palmation.
	b.	Heads less than normal for local quality.	– Full palmation by 5 years, becoming broad with age.
OLD 9 years plus	a.	Poorly developed, irregular or "ugly" heads.	– Well developed antlers with well formed strong palmation and weight in upper antler.
	b.	Good quality heads showing signs of going back for two consecutive years.	
	c.	All bucks of the age 11 - 13 years regardless of quality (better culled than allowed to die).	

Fig.51

SEASON RELATED GUIDE SUMMARY – ROE DEER

		Jan.	Feb.	Mar.	Apr.	May.	Jun.	Jul.	Aug.	Sept.	Oct.	Nov.	Dec.
DOES	Kids / 1 year			Coat change to summer					1st rut	Lose spots – Grow winter coat	Coat change to winter		Tend to form family groups
	2yrs–mature			Change coat to summer				2nd and later ruts		Coat change to winter			
	Old				Change coat to summer					Coat change to winter			
BUCKS	Kids / 1 year			Change coat to summer	Shed knobs start 1st head			Leave mother	Lose spots / 1st rut	Winter coat	Grow buttons on pedicles	Cast antler	
	2yrs–mature				6 points at 3 years / Clean velvet		1 & 2 year old tend to form groups / Start seeking territory		Rut / Rut		Grow winter coat	Cast antler	
									Rut		Grow winter coat	Cast antler / Grow winter coat	
	8 years +			Change to summer coat / Clean velvet	Prime head at 5-6 yrs / Starts going back 6 or 7 plus			Rut / Rut / Rut			Cast antler / Grow winter coat	Cast antler / Grow winter coat	

147

CULL GUIDE SUMMARY – ROE DEER

Fig.52

Age Band	Shootable	Non-shootable
YOUNG Kids-3 years	a. Kids are culled as part of the doe cull, the deciding factor is condition and age of the doe; the total cull number takes priority over quality. b. Yearling with short spikes or buttons c. Yearling numerical cull tales priority over quality. d. 2-year old antlers shorter than ears not tines showing. e. 3 year old short antler less than 6 points.	– Yearling with antlers at least ear length. – 2 year old with at least one tine. – 3 year old with 6 points.
MATURE 4-6 years	Antlers with fewer than 6 points, thin and not well formed.	– Antlers 1½ ear length, 6 points good shape and thickness. (4 points if exceptionally strong)
OLD over 6 years	a. As above. b. Those which show signs of going back of old age (better culled than die).	– Well developed 6 pointers with thick antlers, well pearled and in top condition.

2.5. Records - Statistics - Forecasts

F OREST administration requires a flow of recorded and accurate
data, often large and intricate in volume and content, which when
analysed provides management with the necessary information
flow. In a similar way the recording of deer and related issues is required
for the management of deer.

When deer are managed as a secondary product of forest or a mixed
estate, the information which links the two is that concerning deer
damage, its incidence, location and the crops affected as well as the
damage to non-crop vegetation which may impoverish the habitat. Hence
the recording and monitoring of damage and its relationship with deer
species and numbers are issues of the first importance. Without records
objective assessments and decisions cannot be made.

Monitoring and Reporting Damage

Methodology

In relation to forests deer damage is a sensitive issue on which the
acceptance or rejection of managed deer may depend. Thus proper
recording is important. In small forests and farm woodlands, much of the
necessary information can be memorised; the larger and more complex
structure the forests have, the more unreliable is the memory and all the
more necessary are the records. The importance of records is, however,
relative to (a) the impact of deer on the well-being of the forest, (b) the
importance of deer economics within a given forestry business and (c) the
impact and lasting detrimental effect of grazing, browsing and fraying on
non-croppable vegetation, especially that damage which affects self-
regeneration of self-seeded trees, bushes and shrubs.

The first part of this chapter considers the records useful for economic
deer/trees symbiosis, the second concentrates on deer. Owners and
managers may adopt and adapt those which in their opinion serve their
needs.

Necessary information includes the type of damage, crops affected,
location, incidence, identification of the 'culprits' i.e. the species of
deer or other animals, and identification of the area in relation to the
classification of forest (tree species and age), as well as the position of any

arable crops and their relationship with woodland from which deer may have raided cultivated crops. An important issue here is the durable effect of damage: in relation to trees the chances of survival and of significance of damage, in relation to field crops the extent of the ultimate loss, including the reduced yield from the damaged area. Damage to non-croppable vegetation – the deterioration or regenerating ability of plants, and damage to the environment with despoliation of appearance must also be considered. All this needs to be related to the deer density in the location or vicinity of the damage. Records should be regularly updated and analysed for management use.

Woodland Damage

For accurate, objective, damage recording in woodlands, the method used would be to establish in each class block of the damage sensitive forest a control block, fenced and deer-free. The control block should be about 50 m x 50 m (.25 ha).

Corresponding unfenced .25 ha plots should be established within selected similar forest class areas, one to about 500 ha. Within these blocks damage identified as deer damage can be recorded and compared with the control block. Monitoring should be done when the trees are at their most vulnerable and reduced at later stages of growth. Particularly important is the recording of seasonal damage, and recording as often as four times a year may be required. From the records thus produced damage incidence and value can be established.

This method, whilst pure, may be found uneconomical in small woodland holdings and less accurate variations can be developed. It should be possible to scientifically establish and publish damage models, relating to a variety of forests at different age classes, as guides especially for the use of the smaller forest and woodland owners and foresters.

There are many formats in which the information could be presented – a typical format is below:

Fig.53   WOODLAND DEER DAMAGE RECORD

Date . . . .   Recorded by . . . .

Area	Tree Species	Age	Browsing		Fraying Threshing	Stripping	Deer Species
			Top	Side			

If different deer species are present damage attributable to each should be recorded separately. Where a tree has been damaged more than once each occasion should be singled out. In the damage columns, trees which have died or are dying as a result of damage should be shown in brackets e.g. 25(3), indicating 25 damaged trees with (3) dead or dying. ('Damage' here means suspected long term damage).

Arable Area Damage

The same concept can be used for recording damage to field crops. In the case of cereals, it is necessary to develop a 'bring forward' system which would allow a check on the yield of crops damaged in comparison with undamaged ones.

Fig.54   ARABLE AREAS DEER DAMAGE RECORD

Area	Crop Species	Age at time of damage	Type of damage	Deer No and Species

Non-Arable Area Damage

Fig.55   NON-CROPPABLE VEGETATION DAMAGE RECORD

Area	Type of vegetation	Type and extent of damage	Month	Deer Species

Note:
See also Chapter 3.4 'Care of Habitat'.

Deer Numbers

Whether a full deer count or some other method of estimating deer numbers is used a record of results is needed. The accuracy, and the content of that record will depend on the method used; it could be that where deer are being sighted the record includes quality, sex and age, whereas if the record is based on dung pellet groups or slot counts the total information will be no more than overall numbers divided into species.

Even if only the global number of deer is the fruit of numerical assessment it is possible to make a subsequent estimate of the composition of the deer population by applying the observed sex ratio and the calving rate to the total, these being sometimes obtained from no more than casual, but recorded, observation.

The population record should show the following:

Fig.56   DEER CENSUS RECORD

Method Used . . . .
Species . . . .

Area	Stags/Bucks	Hinds/Does	Calves/Kids	Total

Notes:
1. The 'Area' should be related to the Damage Report (if appropriate).

2. If composition is estimated on the basis of the observed sex ratio and calving rate, indicate (est) after the number.

The deer census record can be enlarged by including detail such as weather conditions, antler shape and size (all useful but difficult to identify and record accurately) and usually would require a clear perception of local standards and conditions and antler quality.

Cull Record

Cull records are of significant importance in several ways. In the first place it is important that each beast culled should be identifiable. The identification should include location where culled under 'Area'. Thus the animal identification will show 'Area' followed by a serial number within the area and sex. The information requirements stated in the 'Individual Cull Record' must be regarded as being the absolute minimum for efficient management planning. There are many additional details which, depending on the degree of management sophistication, could beneficially be included: kidney fat measurement shown as indices on a scale of say 1-5, whether a hind was in milk or dry, where relevant whether the calf/kid was culled or not, age estimation (a) before culling and (b) after, also evidence of injury, disease or parasitic infestation.

Fig.57   INDIVIDUAL CULL RECORD
STAGS/BUCKS

(Minimum requirement)

Area . . . .

Beast Number	Date	Weights		Age	Antler information	
		Gralloched*	Larder*		Tines L R	Other **

* Different weighing may apply on different estates

** There may be a need to include antler weight, length, span; if more detail is needed (e.g. CIC measurements) a separate form would be advisable. If trophy charges are raised the detail here should correspond with the detail on which the trophy charge/fee was raised.

Fig.58   INDIVIDUAL CULL RECORD
HINDS/DOES

(Minimum requirement)

Area . . . .

Beast Number	Date	Weights*		Age	Foetus M/F
		Gralloched	Larder		

The individual Cull Record should be summarised by Area and then by Forest yearly totals. Separate records by species showing Stags/Bucks and Hinds/Does. The example below is for Stags/Bucks only.

153

Fig.59   YEARLY CULL SUMMARY

Forest . . . .

Species . . . .

Area	Age													Total
	C	1	2	3	4	5	6	7	8	9	10	11	12+	

Map Records

Wherever possible data of damage and deer numbers should be recorded not only in a statistical format but also on maps. The maps should all be of a uniform scale and should include details of woodlands (plantation, tree species, age etc.), fields and crops as a support and include correlation of all data. They should show the location of beasts counted/estimated (even if showing no more than the numbers and locations of each culled beast). If observation of individual beasts are shown the details should include species, number by sexes, quality, date etc. Such records are invaluable at the time of cull for they show the concentrations of deer in different parts of the forest/estate and indicate whether the cull needs to be concentrated or whether it should be dispersed.

Photographic Record

It is very useful to support the recorded information by photographs. Antlers cannot be kept forever and photographs of each antler, face on and sideways, taken against a white board with a grid of 2 or 5 cm, provide a good historical record of antler quality and size. Antlers should be identified by Area/Number so that they can be related to other records. This method of recording allows changes in the quality of beast/antler to be monitored which is particularly important as proof of results achieved by selective culling or other management policies.

Other Records

In managing deer, other records may be required to monitor in greater detail such issues as population dynamics, movement, poaching, losses to other causes and fertility rates. The records described here are those which are considered essential to successful management of deer on an estate or group of estates jointly managing deer.

Statistics and Forecasting

This is not the place to expound complicated statistics, but it may be useful to outline how basic statistical methods can be used for successful forecasting and efficient deer management.

A variety of records to be kept are recommended in the preceding section of this chapter. Why are these records needed?

There are different reasons for different records and statistics. Simple statistics will allow us to observe trends which will show us how the density of deer influences the rate of damage, and therefore whether deer density has to be reduced to lessen the rate of damage; for illustration a trend developed from yearly records is shown on pages 100 and 101.

In financial budgeting we must know what income and expenditure has been incurred in managing deer. By themselves these records are dry, but in conjunction with such other records as weights and prices of venison, not only do they allow us to plan the budget, but also to monitor the weights in relation to age, for here is a part of the quality story. If we can increase the weights, not only will the income increase but also we have an indicator of improving quality.

In a similar fashion records of antlers showing weight, number of points and length and spread (perhaps with CIC scores), especially when backed with photographs, is a record of excellence which will help in establishing the market value of trophy or letting fees. Age related antler records will, over a period of time, demonstrate whether there is an improvement for quality which can be correlated with density and, where deer are fed, the extent of feeding.

Records of changing woodland structures related to deer density are also useful in that they help to adjust density to the age of woodland.

Essential in our deer counting and estimating is a simple statistical exercise which allows us to predict the population from the record of previous years' counts, expected mortality (from mortality records), the size of cull and level of calving rate. (This is described also on page 97 in the chapter dealing with Deer Counting and Estimating.)

From the sequences of such records simple analysis will indicate trends in the population. The same would apply to all manner of other important records which will enable us to predict trends in damage, values, prices, quality of trophies and many other areas.

Once a store of reliable data has been developed it can be used for forecasting and analysing trends in many areas. For example the lines on the population graphs on pages 100 and 101 can be projected to predict future population levels (assuming that all other factors remain constant). It would then be possible to calculate the size of cull required to increase or decrease population growth by a given amount. Another important benefit from analysing records is the highlighting of errors which allows for corrective measures to be taken before the errors are compounded by the passage of time.

The following table demonstrates a simple method of predicting the following year's population from deer census, calving rate, sex ratio, culling level and mortality data.

Fig.60   POPULATION FORECAST

	Stags	Hinds	Calves	Total
Numbers year 1				
as at March count	200	250	100	550
plus calving year 1			100	
(at 40% of hinds)				
last year's calves				
to adults	50	50		
Pre-cull population	250	300	100	650
less Cull	70	90	20	180
Mortality 2%	4	8	2	14
Expected population				
March year 2	176	202	78	456

(This approach is similar to that presented on page 97.)

2.6. *Methodology of Damage Prevention in Practice As Risk Insurance*

Damage Prevention

THERE IS grave concern in many minds that deer damage is the main deterrent against planting woodlands. The deepest concern is amongst that circle of nature lovers who cannot accept that control of deer for the benefit of deer themselves and for the benefit of trees, or timber if you like, is ideologically and emotionally acceptable. There are some in the farming, and even the forestry, community who do not believe that damage can be contained through control of deer density. Others seek total risk insurance against damage and go to great lengths and expense to protect their trees. Finally there are those who, in order to protect third party interests and, let us face it, at the same time to ensure that their deer do not stray, fence them in; by the same token they protect what they regard as their property – deer (strictly speaking, in law, live deer on the open range are not the landowner's property; they only become so when they are killed on the owner's land).

With fences at up to £10 a metre at today's prices to erect, and at a significant cost to maintain, the decision to fence permanently should not be taken lightly. There is good evidence that with a good forest layout planned for deer, the risk of damage by deer can be so drastically reduced as to make permanent fencing unnecessary. There always is a risk, however, that more deer than wanted will inhabit a forest, not because of poor management, but primarily because of expanding colonisation and migration.

Increasingly temporary fencing is being resorted to for protection which is well below 100% proof but is sufficient as a short-term measure. Such fencing could be needed mainly to protect newly established forest blocks, or to deter deer from straying. In some areas old fences are not even removed, but allowed to perish when they have outlived their usefulness. In the section in which fencing is discussed we shall consider the use of short-life as well as electric fencing and the concept of no fencing, and weigh up the pros and cons of each.

In the long run we have to accept that in spite of its cost permanent fencing is the only near-totally effective measure. Of course one cannot insure against carelessness and foolishness. Employees who leave gates open, do-gooders who for mischief, misplaced idealism or even through feeling sorry for deer seeking shelter, cut fences and let the beasts in or out. Once in the forest – never out.

A no-fencing policy seems an inviting proposition for those who understand the principles of deer control and capacity. It would seem then that this policy is appropriate and 'environment friendly' in that it does not spoil the appearance of the countryside.

Probably the most doubtful solution in the British climate is the chemical deterrent; for so far no deterrent capable of standing up to prolonged wet weather has been produced. Those which last longest need a brush application and are therefore manpower costly. They are highly coloured and are therefore unsightly and with their comparatively short effective life they are not suited to large scale use. At best, for application in small areas such as infilling or small farm woodlands, they may be acceptable.

Forest Design

It is with trepidation that I approach this section. I am a 'deer man' and not a forester. And yet here am I trying to put ideas to owners and managers on how they should think about their forests with deer in mind. But basically I am not addressing established foresters. My aim is to persuade those who are concerned with existing forest or those who may be thinking of planning new ones, even farm woodlands, to think and plan with deer (and possibly game) in mind. They can be encouraged to treat deer and game as a potentially viable crop producing an annual income, whereas the forest yields its crop after many years.

In this context I also have to accept and admit, that not being a forester, not only may I use the wrong jargon but also commit other *faux pas*.

My objective is to give an outline of the structure of forest planning parameters which should enable deer to become a secondary, viable product within the business of forestry. What I hope to show is that with reliable and suitable planning and with only a comparatively small additional cost and small sacrifices of resources (space perhaps), deer can be turned from a pest into a profitable contributor to the overall business of the forest.

In the present day business scenario the conceptual interrelationship between agriculture and forestry (which has been outlined already in Chapter 1.1) suggests that, perhaps, forestry would be a more inviting proposition as an alternative use of land if it offered more revenue between the establishment and cropping stages. For those who wish to use their investment capital for growth and who are concerned about taxation, forestry as a business proposition is advantageous, but it is changing, becoming increasingly liberal and environmentally friendly from year to year.

In those instances where forestry is looked upon as an alternative use of agricultural land, the possibility of creating an income throughout the stages of establishment and maturation, must be regarded as an inviting opportunity.

A proportion of this work concentrates on deer as a possible by-product of the forest, creating income. To realise such income, however, some rethinking and reshaping of traditionally held attitudes and a sounder appreciation of deer is needed.

In this chapter we concentrate our attention on forestry itself and on creating a habitat for deer (and other game) compatible with modern management methods. To this end comparatively simple changes to the traditionally accepted planning parameters of forestry are suggested. These are made easier by the recent thinking in forestry circles – the concept of landscaping. The two main issues which must be addressed are a supportive habitat for deer and suitable facilities for the culling of deer as a crop.

Here one has to pay tribute to the Forestry Commission, who in the last decade have adjusted their thinking and have blazed the trail, albeit quietly, towards the creation of a deer supportive, deer friendly habitat. The greatest differences between the old and the new thinking include the planting of a greater mix of trees, more broadleaves, wider espacement, more and wider rides, more attention to landscaping and consideration for wildlife. Most of these are backed by generous and far-sighted incentives and grants from the Government.[21] [22] Many a farmer, however, who might consider woodlands as an alternative use of land may not be fully aware of the requirements which are essential for the benefit of deer and game.

Food within the Habitat

First and foremost is the need for a feeding platform which is not the forest crop. The provision of feeding areas consisting of grasses, herbs and shrubs or even 'disposable' trees which are attractive to deer and grown in adequate quantities to support the population is required.

There are those who believe that, because 100 farmed red deer can live on 25 ha of well balanced pasture of high quality grass, the hill or forest can support a similar number. They forget that farm deer are also intensively fed on supplements.

[21] *Forest and Conservation* (FC Environmental Leaflet, 1989, HMSO).
[22] Hart, C., *Practical Forestry* (Allan Sutton, 1991).

However, the 25 ha concept can be applied to wild deer in a forest. If 25 ha, seeded with a grass/herb mixture, is designated for deer feeding in a forest of say 2,500 ha (1% of area) then, with a density of between four and six red deer per 100 ha, the grazing provided could sustain over 100 deer (proportionally more with smaller species). From this a model can be developed which allows for the designation of about 1% of a forest for fields and rides, cultivated and sown with a suitable grass/herb seed mixture, specifically for deer grazing. By providing this attractive feeding facility deer can be distracted from browsing on the tree crop; there is proof, based on observation and the recording of the incidence of deer damage in many Continental forests, that where good pastures are provided damage can be significantly reduced.

Rides and Tracks as Feeding Areas

In a forest block a proportion of the area is usually devoted to rides and tracks. If two metre wide strips at the edges are devoted to a good variety of grasses a start will be made for creating a deer feeding platform. However, long straight rides, or worse still, wide straight firebreaks do not give deer a sufficient measure of safety. Rides are too open and are often draughty, leaving deer exposed and vulnerable; deer feel it! A ride or firebreak fifteen metres wide requires lines of shrubs, probably half of its width and alternating between the two sides, as visual shelters. Rides are a useful contribution towards the pastures needed but they cannot be the only source of the aforementioned 20-25 ha per 2,500 ha of forest.

Fig.61   FOREST RIDES – LAYOUT

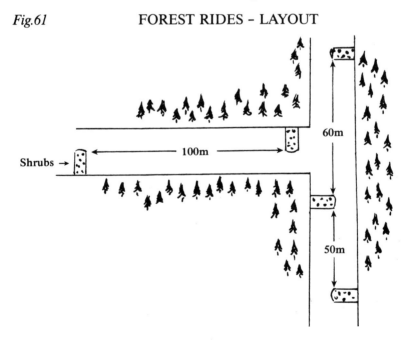

Feeding Fields

The primary reason for deer damage is the satisfaction of physiological needs; of hunger, common to all living beings, the cleaning of the velvet on antlers, which is peculiar to deer, and a pre-rut or mating display, which is a characteristic, in one form or other, of many creatures. In the drive to satisfy these needs deer graze, browse, fray and thresh.

We cannot stop these damaging activities in healthy deer, but we can provide a habitat so structured that a significant proportion is concentrated on trees and other vegetation designated for this purpose. This is done mainly through the provision of feeding fields, rides and margin planting.

The purpose of feeding fields is to provide food needed by the deer interspersed with shrubs, trees and bushes to provide for antler cleaning. In this way a reduction of damage through browsing and fraying/ threshing is achieved. The advantages are multiple; the feeding fields provide for deer even during the forest's most inhospitable period, which follows the thicket stage and lasts for many years. Hence the changes in the age-related feeding potential of the woodland blocks, which may cause migration, become less important in relation to deer. The fields help to localise deer in areas designated for them to the extent that even after felling and subsequent re-establishment, deer do not automatically gravitate to the new Eldorado in the newly established plantation in search of food. The 'regular diet' so provided at the very least decreases damage and deer have a continuity of feed which provides for a better retention of those qualities in deer which are attributable to feeding. Additionally it is easier to carry out regular, accurate and planned culling.

There are two approaches to the provision of feeding fields; one so to speak incidental, the other planned. The incidental approach simply suggests that planting failures are not 'made good' but are designated as feeding areas. It is said that planting failures amount to 10% and if this is right, and provided the failures are concentrated and not spread widely as single tree failures, they would, in terms of area, be ample. We have to protect, however, against failure areas caused by poor or otherwise unsuitable soil. On such soils pastures are unlikely to grow better than trees. The other approach is to include at the planning stage the provision of feeding areas and treating failures as additions to these areas.

The advantages of the planned approach are clear. Firstly there is no need to wait for failures to occur and secondly if they do not happen, feeding fields are already there having been prepared and established as such.

There are important characteristics of feeding fields which need to be taken into account. For success they must provide not only attractive feeding, but must also provide deer with a sense of natural security, i.e. not be completely open spaces uninterrupted by trees or bushes as rides often are. They must provide suitable shrubs, bushes or even trees, on which antlers can be cleaned within the feeding area.

The planning and establishment of feeding fields calls, therefore, for a little imagination. The grazing provided needs to be a mixture which is attractive throughout the year (as far as is possible); the shape should be irregular and broken by the planting of shrubs, bushes and trees within the area, giving it the appearance of a good value natural surrounding. It should give a feeling of security, provide for antler cleaning and give an adequate clear field of vision for culling. To this end areas of about 100 m across (approximately 1 ha) are probably ideal.

Experience suggests that red deer (and perhaps also sika) take more easily to feeding fields if these provide them with a greater feeling of security than that which is required by roe deer. The feeding fields for red and sika deer should be somewhat larger and more broken up by bushes and trees, but allowing a good field of vision for spotting danger as well as for competing stags during the rut.

The dispersion of feeding fields should be planned so that they are in the proximity of current or future new plantings (say within 500 m), thus being linked to the structural classes. The area allowance should be in the region of 20-25 ha for every 100 red deer, and at a density level four red deer per 100 ha of forest. In this allocation of space for feeding, grass-seeded rides may be included as a part of the requirement but at least three-quarters should be in the form of feeding fields. These areas are suggested on the basis of them being cultivated from time to time and sown with suitable deer attractive vegetation (see Annex 1 to this chapter). Feeding fields in areas of good soil, would probably regenerate sufficiently to remain maintenance free for several years other than perhaps top dressing. On poor soil re-cultivation every few years would be called for. It is not suggested, however, that the entire area of the feeding fields should be cultivated and sown with 'choice' vegetation, much of it can rely on natural self-regeneration.

If the rides are sown with good quality grasses they should be broken up with shrubs as suggested. Provision of feeding fields need not be a total sacrifice of tree space – suitable river banks, steep slopes with rock outcrops and other ground marginally suitable for tree planting can be used for this purpose provided that ground is prepared and sown/planted. These locations tend to be more easily accepted by deer than artificial fields for they are usually of a more natural appearance.

Some say that feeding fields do not work as damage prevention measures. These opinions tend to originate from forests which, in terms of the deer densities suggested here, are significantly overpopulated. It follows, therefore, that for success deer density of an order far lower than is usual in Britain is required. In the British climate there should be no need

Fig 62   FEEDING FIELDS
                   NATURAL APPEARANCE NEEDED

to make special provision for additional winter feeding as practised in many Continental countries where deep snow is common.

The announcement by the Government in July 1990, that the Forestry Commission will allow as grant-worthy the inclusion of significant open areas within new planting supports the ideas presented in this section.

Prevention of Fraying and Threshing

While considering forest design for deer it is worth paying some attention to decreasing the danger from fraying and threshing. The physiological needs vented through fraying and threshing can be targeted by providing deer with expendable shrubs, bushes and trees of no economical importance, some of which could be fruit bearing for additional food value. Ideally these have to be located on the margins of the woodland, along the rides and roads, or within and around the feeding fields. Underplanting within the forest is usually also very helpful.

It is not likely that this measure will completely eliminate threshing or fraying but, at comparatively low cost, and with low deer density level as already discussed, it will significantly reduce damage.

Rides and Feeding Fields for Cull and Observation

One of the big problems which forest deer management has is fulfilling the cull targets, which is just as difficult as conducting deer counts (by whichever method). It is a matter of 'visibility' in dense planting even with increased espacement. Invariably deer are aware of the stalker's presence before the stalker sees the deer, thus culling becomes something of a 'hit and miss' effort and, of necessity, becomes non-selective in order to achieve the basic numerical control target.

Rides and feeding fields provide facilities essential for culling. Whether or not high seats are used for observation or culling will depend largely on the type of terrain taking all considerations of safety into account. Usually some high seats are useful, even in undulating land.

If rides and feeding fields are to allow for culling it is necessary to have suitable access. There is little point in crashing through dense woodland to reach a quiet spot on the edge of a feeding field or a well designed ride. Access in the form of stalking paths, about two metres wide (similar to the width of espacement) is needed and can be easily provided. Stalking paths should be clear of obstructions such as ground litter twigs and leaves, and overhanging branches need to be cleaned up. A small tractor or all terrain vehicle with suitable attachments is probably the most efficient method of maintaining them. The paths should terminate at the ride or field behind the high seats, butts or whatever other vantage points can be provided.

Streams, Rivers and Marginal Areas

Everything that has been said above can also be applied to the banks of streams and rivers cutting through forests. In large forests there is an increasing tendency to leave as much as a 100 m strip unplanted, thus providing a good natural feeding field where deer can be observed and culled and where 'guns' can be positioned for bird drives. High seats can be located at suitable sites.

Other Benefits

With the exception of high seats, everything that is done for deer will benefit other game from the point of view of feeding, shooting and holding. Not only will game birds benefit but also all manner of other fauna and flora which otherwise find forests an inhospitable habitat. This apart, such open areas are a pleasing landscaping improvement.

High Seats

The use of high seats in woodland areas has become popular if for no other reason than because they facilitate the cull. The location of a high seat should ideally be at the very edge of woodland, at the termination of or adjoining a stalking path. It should have adequate camouflage, natural or artificial, to allow the 'rifle' to enter and leave without being spotted. The seat has to be within observation and shooting range of the deer but not so close that the smallest human movement can be detected by the nearby animals. Here we have to remember that it is not only deer who matter; other animals may be alerted by movement and alert the deer without our being aware of it.

High seats have to conform by law with the requirements of the Health and Safety at Work Act. The owner is responsible for the adequacy of their construction and the safety of the occupant. There are several types of manufactured seats on the market, many of them transportable. Transportable seats are often useful when selecting a suitable location for the permanent seat.

All manner of home-made seats have been erected by owners and stalkers and it is difficult to give constructional details but a few tips may be useful.

The ladder to the high seat compartment requires a number of rungs, these should be spaced so as to allow easy mounting. They must be sturdy enough not to creak and crack and must be nailed and lashed to the uprights (lashing is an insurance against rusted nails). The sitting plank should be movable so that when it is not in use it does not collect water and bird droppings. It must be sturdy so that small movements do not make it creak. There should be a shooting rail across the front sufficiently substantial for use as a hand and rifle rest. The floor must be sturdy enough to allow for the silent movement of feet. Nylon matting which absorbs noise and does not rot in wet weather, can be of benefit.

It is often convenient to have a peg or hook on which to hang items of clothing and sometimes a small shelf can be handy.

Many foresters and owners object to high seats being directly attached to trees. Such attachments usually effected with nails, wires or even nylon ropes, damage the trees sooner or later and are also of doubtful value in strong winds. All this means that the safest seat is a free-standing permanent one, perhaps between the trees.

Fencing

In forest design fencing must be considered, this being one of the forms of damage protection.

Firstly, fencing should be erected at a sufficient distance from the trees to prevent windblown trees damaging the fence and creating openings for deer. Secondly, in areas affected by winter blizzards, fences should be so located that snow drifts do not cover the fence. To this end it may be cost effective to allow for some feeding areas along the fence, especially where the fence or the edge of the planting are not in long straight lines. In hilly areas it is very important to ensure that deer cannot jump the fence from higher ground outside the fence. Thirdly, it is important to allow for deer leaps to enable deer to get in or out of the fenced area as appropriate. Deer leaps need to be planned in advance and provision should also be made for additional ones when regular movements become established.

When the forest is being created, or has been created, between deer wintering and summer grounds (barring deer from habitual rutting stands and thus forcing long detours) downfalls should be provided to permit deer to move along traditional routes. This is particularly important where long but comparatively narrow blocks have been fenced. Downfalls are a facilitating provision but they can also be a saving. Deer have been known to break the fence or even jump it in an attempt to reach their wintering ground, to avoid severe weather, to reach the rutting stand or even just to get away from flies or midges and sometimes human interference. Such fence breaks can be expensive because often they are not discovered before major penetration has taken place.

A problem with fencing is gates are frequently left open, whether for convenience, laziness, oversight or sheer stupidity. Large self-shutting gates are expensive. With the increasing incidence of hikers an access facility needs to be provided. Increasingly it is being found that well constructed and well maintained stiles, even over a high red deer fence, are preferable to the risk of open gates. Owners are responsible for the construction of stiles and their compliance with Health and Safety Regulations but an appropriate disclaiming notice, especially against improper use, may offer at least some protection.

In recent years deer leaps have found revival in many circles as being a useful adjunct to fencing. They were widely used in deer parks in bygone years to let deer enter the walled or fenced perimeter. The Red Deer Commission[23] gives some useful technical advice.

The deer leap construction, location and appearance must be natural and, therefore, not intimidating and the top on the take-off side should be a small flat platform with the rising slope gentle; it should be grassed, even planted with shrubs (therefore not left as bare timber planks which are not only unnatural but slippery when wet and noisy when hollow underneath). The vertical face at the fence should not reach the fence top height by 30-40 cm, and should be close enough to the fence to not

[23] Red Deer Commission, *Annual Report 1986* (HMSO, 1988).

Fig 63   DEER LEAP

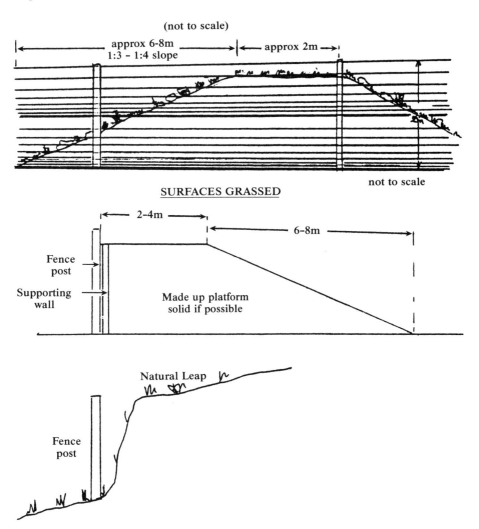

(not to scale)

approx 6-8m
1:3 – 1:4 slope

approx 2m

SURFACES GRASSED

not to scale

2-4m

6-8m

Fence post

Supporting wall

Made up platform solid if possible

Natural Leap

Fence post

allow a deer to get wedged in between.

If possible natural terrain irregularities of the ground can be used as a part of the structure.

Dropping Fences

The same Report[23] also devotes space to the concept of dropping fences. The idea is not new; it amounts to constructing sections of fence in such a way that they can be quickly dropped or removed and then re-erected.

When deer break into an enclosure a section of the fence, strategically positioned, is dropped and deer are driven out through the gap. Once the deer are out the section is re-erected.

The Commission suggests that this type of arrangement can be seen as a counter-measure to mass break-ins when deer are seeking shelter from bad weather or during mass seasonal movements endangering the fence. This notion presupposes that the direction of the movement is adequately predictable at the time the fencing is being installed to allow for the inclusion of dropping sections in places where they may be needed.

Note:

If, from local knowledge, deer movements can be predicted, it would be equally effective to provide a series of well sited deer leaps. It would also seem more efficient to include in the forest plan deer downfalls along the expected route of deer movement.

Annex 1 to Chapter 2.6.

Feeding Fields, Seeds, Shrubs and Trees for Deer
based on R. Prior [24]

Feeding Fields

Fodder root mixture for use on medium to good agricultural land with a reasonable application of compound fertilisers. The constituents are reasonably winter-hardy and may last until January; sow May and June.

Fig 64a   DEER FEED – SEED MIXTURES

1 kg Thousand Headed Kale
1 kg Maris Kestrel Kale
½ kg Purple Top Swede
½ kg Giant Rape
½ kg Tyfon Stubble Turnip
¼ kg Green Globe Turnip
(Apply 3¾ kg per acre = 9¼ kg per hectare)

Fodder root mixture for upland areas and less fertile conditions. This mixture requires reasonable soil and will not thrive in very acid soils; sow in July.

3½ kg Giant Rape
½ kg Green Globe Turnip
6 kg Danish Italian Ryegrass
(Apply 9½ kg per acre = 23½ kg per hectare)

Grasses and Clovers

For use in rides or as a supplement in the feeding fields:

Bent grass	Lucerne	Timothy
Clover alsike	Meadow smooth	Trefoil
Fescue	Ryegrass, perennial	Yorkshire fog
Foxtail	Sainfoin	

[24] Prior, R., *Trees and Deer* (Batsford, 1983).

169

Grass mixture for poor soil

In poor soil conditions (hill areas of high rainfall, woodland rides of sandy soil). Tolerates acidity but herbage will be more palatable if limed from time to time.

> 3½ kg Highland Bent
> 5½ kg Creeping Red Fescue
> 2½ kg Sheeps Fescue
> 2½ kg Smooth-stalked Meadow Grass
> ¼ kg Birds Foot Trefoil
> ¼ kg Wild White Clover
> (Apply 14½ kg per acre = 35¾ kg per hectare)

Fig 64b   DEER FEED – HERBS AND TREES
ATTRACTIVE TO DEER

Herbs

Anemone	Dandelion	Rosebay willow herb
Brooklime	Knotweed	Sorrel
Campion red	Lupin, sweet	Strawberry
Campion white	Meadowsweet	Vetch purple milk
Celandine	Redleg	Violet
Cinquefoil hoary	Ribwort	Yarrow

Trees and shrubs

Alder buckthorn	Dogwood	Maple, Norway
Apple	Elder	Oak
Aspen	Gean	Pine, lodgepole
Beech	Guelder rose	Poplar
Bog myrtle	Hawthorn	Rowan
Bramble	Hazel	Spindle
Broom	Holly	Wayfaring tree
Cherry, bird	Hornbeam	Whitebeam
Chestnut, sweet	Maple, field	Willow

Current and local experience may suggest that the following are also deer attractive in a given locality:

Fir, Douglas   Fir, Grand   Larch   Spruce, Norway

Trees and shrubs which deer are reluctant to eat are: alder, birch, honeysuckle (Japanese), pine (Austrian or Corsican), juniper, shallon, snowberry and rhododendron.

Fig 64c   RANKING ORDER OF TREE PREFERENCES
BY RED DEER
Dzieciolowski [24b]

	Highly preferred	Preferred	Seldom used
Sablina 1959 White Russia	Willow Aspen Ash Oak	Rowan Birch	Lime Hornbeam
Dzieciolowski 1970 Poland	Sessile oak Willow Rowan Hazel	Norway maple Hornbeam Cherry Alder	Scots pine Juniper
Bobek, Weiner, Zielinski 1972 Poland	Aspen Willow Alder, buckthorn	Oak	Lime Hornbeam Birch
Ahlen 1965 S. Sweden	Ash Willow Alder, buckthorn	Norway spruce Birch	Alder
Chard 1966 N-W England	Juniper Red oak Pine Norway spruce	Larch Sycamore Scots pine Oak Birch	Sitka spruce Beech Alder
Ueckerman 1960 W. Germany	Poplar Oak Fir Norway maple Ash Red oak	Scots pine Norway spruce Beech Fir, Douglas Larch	Sitka spruce Alder Silver birch

Note:
   Some tree species appear in more than one column above, suggesting
   that there are some local preferences.

[24b] Dzieciolowski, R., *Diet of European Red Deer* (Polish Ecol. Studies 2; 33-50, &
IBL 365).

Annex 2 to Chapter 2.6.

Fencing Specification

There are some aspects of fencing, including general specification, upon which both foresters and those interested in deer agree.

The Red Deer Commission[23] and Forestry Commission[25] suggest the following:

Line Wire Fencing

On low ground where fences can be regularly inspected 11-wire fence of steel spring wire with wire droppers, which lock on to the horizontal wires, at one metre intervals and have ends twisted round the wire are suitable. Staples or wooden droppers are not recommended. Posts should be not more than 10 m (30 ft) apart, with strainers at intervals of 350 m (1,100 ft).

Two-piece Netting

Rylock type hinged joint or welded mesh to a minimum of 1.8 m (6 ft), strung on three wires of spring steel and attached to wire lashing rods. Posts in hilly country should not be more than 5 m (16 ft) apart with strainers not more than 200 m (650 ft) apart. This interval can be exceeded over level ground which is not subject to snow drifting.

One-piece Netting

The continual type strung on three spring steel line wires and attached by lashing rods. The spacing of posts and strainers should be as for the two-piece netting fence.

Sheep Netting

An alternative to welded mesh or rylock type, but the 14 gauge which is needed tends to be expensive.

Combined Fencing

18 gauge rabbit netting backed by not less than four steel line wires with

[25] Pepper, W. & Lee, L., *Forest Fencing* (FC Pamphlet 80, HMSO, 1988).

172

C6/90/30 rylock type on the bottom and hinged or welded mesh on the top.

The Forestry Commission recognises two basic types of deer fencing, both are recommended to be 2.8 m high; Light specification for roe deer and Heavy specification for the larger species.

Roe Deer (Light) Fence: Lower half – netting: woven field, hinge joint or ring lock, galvanised, pattern C6/90/30. Upper half: galvanised hexagonal mesh 900 mm wide. 75 mm mesh size, 1 mm (19 gauge) wire.

Red Deer (Heavy) Fence: Lower half – woven field, hinge joint or ring lock, galvanised, pattern C6/90/15 or C8/80/15. Upper half – woven field, hinge joint or ring lock, galvanised, pattern C6/90/30.

Much information will be found in Hart[22] and FC Pamphlet 80[25] where Hart also quotes with specifications as below:

	Woven wire mesh	Welded wire mesh	
Upper	C8/80/30 C6/90/30 HT8/80/39	FF3 FF5	FC2 FC3
Lower	C8/80/15 C7/10/15 HT88/80/15	FF1 FC1	

Note:
 For roe, normal sheep type netting (C6/90/30 or C6/80/15) topped up with hexagonal mesh not lower than 1.8 m may be adequate where deer are not unduly disturbed in the habitat. In disturbed areas higher fencing is advisable. Fallow and sika deer require fencing of the red deer type as described above.

Electric Fencing

1. Current should be 5000 v pulsing from the mains or heavy duty battery of 12 v (one battery energises up to 6 km (3.6 miles)).
2. The earthing must take into account the type of undersoil.
3. The ground immediately under the fence should be cleaned and periodically sprayed with herbicide to avoid shorts from wet vegetation.
4. Ideally there should be either a light reflecting wire or light reflecting tape in the fence to make it visible from a distance.
5. It has been found useful to add a stand-off strand of wire 1 m away from the fence and 1 m above the ground. Stand-off wire need not be electrified, but when electrified it does increase effectiveness; this wire is less effective on brackets than if mounted on short stakes about 1 m from the main fence.

6. The height of electric fencing should be the same as non-electric and a topping strand of electrified wire has proved a useful additional protection.
7. The distances between the strands, going from ground level should be 20 cm, 20 cm, 40 cm, 40 cm, 40 cm, 40 cm. This means that the ground vegetation below the fence needs to be very strictly controlled.
8. Electrified wires can be incorporated in standard wire fencing with at least three electrified lines being included at the bottom, and the top wire being also electrified.

Electric fencing is gaining popularity and Rutland Electric Fencing Co of Oakham (Leics) (and Rutland Electric Fencing (Scotland) of Brechin, Angus) provide a number of specifications. Among them is a standard 180 cm red deer fence with an addition of two strand electrified wire fence 90 cm high and 50-100 cm away from the main fence. (Cost of wire fence erected seems very competitive).

They also produce anti-marauding fence claimed to be effective against both red and roe deer which is a combination of two electrified fences 1 m high and 65 cm apart on square sawn timber posts.

ELECTRIC SHEEP NETTING IS NOT SUITABLE FOR DEER AND SHOULD NEVER BE USED the reason being that deer are inclined to crawl under a fence, the males lying their antlers along the shoulder when bellying under or attempting to squeeze through the eyes. Invariably they become entangled. The females are less vulnerable but cases of them being strangled by fencing are on record.

Fence Costing

Like many other land use industry costings the presentation of fencing costs is difficult. Some owners use their own staff, others use contractors; some are close to the sources of materials, others a long way off. These overheads have a significant influence on overall fence costs.

2.7. Deer of Hill and Woodland

I N THE preceeding chapters, whilst discussing deer and the methods of looking after their welfare the differences between woodland and hill have been emphasised several times.

The different management problems which apply to hill and woodland deer will be discussed in Part 3, but it is appropriate here to highlight some basic differences in deer management practice.

Species

Hill deer are in the main the red deer of the Scottish Highlands and Islands, but there are pockets of sika deer.

There have been a few occasions when roe deer took to the hills after being fenced out from afforestation areas, either at the establishment stage or during replanting. These deer however, never changed their habits and did not remain on the hill for long. Usually, during the first or second winter, exposed to the rigours of the climate and requiring more energy than other species because of the physiology of their antler development and pregnancy they either perished or moved to woodland cover.

Development

Because of climatic differences and the quality of habitat, including food and shelter, woodland deer grow larger and generally stronger than hill deer. Scottish upland forest deer are more like their hill brothers and sisters than their lowland and English woodland cousins, the major difference between the upland forest and hill habitats being shelter, not food. The differences between hill and English woodland deer are much more pronounced; body and antler weights can be up to 50% greater, the survival rate 20-30% better and females conceiving at an earlier age.

Herd Life

Scottish hill deer tend to congregate in large herds. We said elsewhere that 50-100 hinds in one herd is not considered very large and that herds of 300

175

PLATE 8   SCOTTISH HILL AND
ENGLISH WOODLAND DEER ANTLERS

in winter are known but are exceptional. Stags also live in herds which are never as large as hind herds. Deer find life in numbers safer, having more eyes and ears to warn of danger. In adverse weather like snow, large herds find it easier to make paths through snow or rummage in the snow for food and in very cold windy weather they crowd into gullies and other shelter in close body contact to maintain body temperature.

Just about the opposite is true of woodland. Large herds have greater difficulty concealing themselves and herds of a dozen are regarded as large. They have less of a problem with feeding, even in winter, for under the tree canopy among the taller herbs and bushes they can always find some food, and at worst take to bark stripping.

We have already covered some details of deer management. We have said that whilst it is acceptable for hill deer to be managed at the 'deer for venison' sex ratio of one stag to three or more hinds, such a ratio is not acceptable in woodland because of the high cull that it generates. Even if the forest were to be landscaped for deer it would be bad practice.

We have also said that because the calving and calf survival rate is higher in woodlands, the cull expressed as a percentage of population must be higher in the forest than on the hill. It also increases the need for the culling of calves/kids.

We have agreed that in a situation of excessive population it may be prudent and necessary to abandon selection in culling, concentrating all efforts on a numerical cull as a means of reducing the population, with a hind/doe cull being given priority. In woodland this is even more important due to greater difficulty in spotting and culling. In discussing the practicalities of deer management it has to be recognised that there are in fact three, and not just two, situations in which deer have to be differently handled:

1. Hill Deer
2. Highland forest deer
3. Lowland and English forest deer

Hill Deer

The 'Monarch of the Glen' is a rare sight today. For the last four decades, if not longer, hill deer have lost land to forestry and other industries, and at the same time their numbers have grown threefold. This is not the place to discuss why but it is the place, however, to discuss how hill deer should be – perhaps should have been – managed.

A high proportion of hill deer share their range with sheep so they are in competition with sheep for food. It is no good saying that sheep graze on different vegetation. The facts are that deer, or sheep and deer, having grazed the hill have left it in many instances bereft of much valuable growth. This encourages the growth of bracken, molinia and other grasses and herbs which neither will eat. Often, the only remaining natural vegetation is heather, and this is grazed from the top, loses its flowering shoot before flowers appear, before seeds are formed, and before any regeneration can start.

Without the heather seed burning results in further spread of bracken and molinia. On better soils with regenerating heather, the young and supple growth is quickly demolished by the grazers. Such is the state of play, that on some hills the August and September heather colouring of the hill is a matter of nostalgic memory, whilst the cackle of grouse is no longer heard, they also having been deprived of heather and heather-living insects. As a result, one has to consider the capacity of the hill.

In most locations deer are managed with the sex ratio geared to hind preponderance. This is in the hope that by producing a high number of calves more stags will be produced for stalking, and more venison to sell. It does mean, however, that the hill population has become younger overall. With the venison market affected by events such as Chernobyl in 1986, to a slump in the market in 1989 and 1990, a lowering of the hind cull is producing an increasing number of unwanted calves. For years stalking stags was a sporting attraction, whilst the culling of hinds was treated with a lesser degree of urgency.

The practicalities of control of hill deer are simple. It is comparatively easy to count (literally count) deer on the hill. The count result may not be 100% accurate but with experience it should be within a 5% margin. Culling is also comparatively easy in that deer can be sighted (spied) at long distance, and with a knowledge of the terrain and intricacies of wind and weather, stalked to a comfortable shooting distance – the shot being taken lying down with a support for the rifle. An experienced stalker can, if need be, take out several beasts from a herd at one attempt (this is often done with hind stalking but less often with stags who need more careful selection).

A common problem with grassed beasts is the recovery of carcasses. Dragging is increasingly frowned upon because it damages the venison (the new EC regulations would not pass as fit for consumption venison which shows signs of damage). 'All terrain' vehicles are, therefore, widely used in place of ponies, being both greater in capacity and cheaper in manpower.

Hind stalking often suffers because the attentions of the professional stalker/keeper are diverted from the hind cull to bird shooting. The culling of hinds is therefore left until the winter when days are short, weather is often poor, and the beasts are run down and in comparatively poor condition.

Upland Forest Deer

There is a sequence of facts in the recent history of Scottish forests which has to be taken into account in order to understand the state of play regarding deer and their management.

Until a few years ago the forest planting policy was for uniform, single species, close planting of very large areas, usually fenced against deer. One way or another deer managed to get in – it may have been that windblows damaged fences, that fences were not adequately maintained or that in winter snow drifts covered the fence and allowed access. It matters not how deer got in – they did !

Initially attempts were made to exterminate them. Because of the density of the forests, with few open spaces, the attempts failed. Attempts to 'manage' the deer failed equally and for similar reasons. Few if any foresters had any idea of how many deer their forests held. The estimates were often so low that even limited culling produced more deer culled than were counted. In Galloway Forest, where some 600-800 red deer were estimated to live, more than that number were culled in two years and a Vantage Point Count in the late 1980s established over 2,000 within the boundaries of the forest.

In some forests red deer density equalled that of the hill, with little food available under the closed canopy except for the margins and a few rides. At that high density deer were doing untold damage through stripping, as well as breaking out and marauding agricultural land.

It is only in recent years that, under the guidance of the Forestry Commission, forest landscaping has been introduced in the new and even in established forests. The establishment of feeding fields, wide grassed rides, observation towers and high seats to facilitate observation and culling of deer have been included. In these forests the staff includes wildlife rangers responsible for deer, and all staff are trained in deer management. This policy encourages the planting of broadleaf trees either as a mixture with conifers or as blocks. It will improve the habitat for deer and certainly will facilitate better, more careful and adequate culling against a background of more accurate estimates executed by a variety of methods, recognising that the holding capacity of forests varies with the forest class. To this day, however, we have not developed in this country a method of establishing acceptable capacities for forests. Hence the culls are on a trial and error basis, probably relating the size of cull to the incidence of damage.

Under the newly developing conditions it will be possible not only to fulfil the cull target (however it be established) but to improve the quality of deer and treat deer as an asset which produces a yearly revenue from sporting lets and venison sales.

The 60,000 ha Kielder Forest (Forestry Commission), much of which has been landscaped with a view to managing deer more effectively amongst other things, is populated by about 7,500 head of roe deer and the Forestry Commission culls about 500 bucks and the same number of does, which yields an annual income of £62,000 a year.[26]

Lowland and English Forest Deer

There is little doubt that, maybe due to deer parks, there has been a better understanding of deer in the Lowlands and England. In consequence the Lowland and English forest is a somewhat happier saga. In the first place forest blocks tend to be smaller. In the second place since the early post-war years it has been recognised that deer can be stalked in woodlands and numerous stalkers have taken advantage of the sport that woodland deer offered (they may have developed the skill and interest by serving with HM Forces, the Civil Service or other organisations on the Continent in the post war years. Certainly the Ministry of Defence has improved its land management efficiency and now has a core of trained stalkers through the Services Branch of the British Deer Society).

However, the problem of deer penetration into commercial forests is not much easier to solve than in Scotland and for the same or similar reasons.

[26] McIntosh, Dr. R., British Deer Society AGM, 1991 and *Roe Deer Management* (Deer, November 1991).

Part Three

Deer Economics

3.1. Management Principles

Management Overview

IF WE ACCEPT that everything that happens within an enterprise ought to be managed, we have to accept that deer, looked upon as an asset which can be and should be used, need to be managed too.

In business terms the management of deer (or game or fishing, or any other secondary activity within an estate) needs to be integrated into the whole. These activities need to be treated as constituent parts, not unlike pigs, cattle, cereal or indeed woodland, each of which has to bring back a profit and stand on its own feet.

Because game shooting and fishing have been a sporting activity, usually subject to vast 'out of pocket' sudsidies by the owner, their status has become different, privileged if you like. Also the employees looking after these activities have tended to have a different 'standing' with both financial and in kind, perks and privileges unknown in the employment of others, who are their 'job equals'.

In the changing economic climate of country life gamekeeping, especially on smaller estates, has increasingly become a part of the job of a woodman or other employee who perhaps has time to spare or an appropriate sporting or wildlife interest. In the same way the deerkeeper or stalker often has other duties to perform as well. The acceptance of these responsibilities by woodmen or foresters is resented but undoubtedly it will become an increasingly accepted compromise. Even game and river keepers look askance at the proposition of deerkeeping duties being tacked on to their other responsibilities, but the days of this type of job demarcation are nearly over. If necessary it may be that this historic combination of traditional perks, privileges and other unique terms of employment will have to be bought-out to put affairs on a proper and more regulated business footing.

For complete success, planned management of deer, game and fisheries needs to be integrated with other activities. There is a good managerial reason for this. Many activities within an estate can be supportive of good game, deer and fish management just as they can destroy it. As many know from their own experience deer, more than the other two, can defeat the primary activities of the estate, e.g. destroy plantations, or a sugar beet field.

Some fertilisers or herbicides can ruin a fishery and act as a deterrent to deer, whilst many field crops can act as supportive game cover provided they are not overdosed with pesticides. Without the integration of interests under unified overall control success may be difficult to achieve.

In terms of accounting there is also a need to integrate. Costs for feed, transport, even wages and other overheads can be 'lost' under many headings, but this does not make good business sense. On some estates even the cost of game and deer taken for the house and stalking or shooting for the house guests are being credited to the departmental accounts to show the true picture.

All this may call for some ingenuity in allocating departmental costs related to one employee supporting two or even three operations. Feed for game or deer may also be a debit to one account and a credit to another. Only with attention to detail will true profitability be discovered.

Ecological and Business Deer Management Objectives

Ecological Objectives

In all activities it is necessary to set objectives against which performance can be measured and management principles established. There are many objectives that can be structured for the management of deer. They can be looked at from a purely ecological standpoint, considering them and their habitat as an ecosystem which needs caring for; alternatively one can adjust the ecological objectives to adapt them, if you like, to business objectives.

The objectives that most definitely control business strategy are:

1. Reduction of numbers – protection of crops and environment.
2. Population restructuring – density, age and sex structure.
3. Venison production.
4. Sporting facilities.
5. Development and maintenance of quality to enhance income or purity of species.
6. Preservation and protection of deer (high damage tolerance) within their habitat (therefore preservation of habitat).

There can be others.

To develop the strategy needed to pursue and achieve the ecological objectives a clear identification of datum points is needed. These relate to, describe and quantify:

A. Area – The size of:
   1. Total range.
   2. Area managed.

B. Deer – size of population:
  1. Total range.
  2. Area managed.

A. Area Information

This consists of the nutritional value of total vegetation over the range and area managed as the feeding platform, plus the probable changes through fencing, forestry – existing and proposed – or any other changes which are likely to affect the feeding potential. Forestry age and species structure is of prime importance in woodland deer management as is climate (probably more of an influence on the hill than in woodland).

B. Deer Information

Present number by species, sex ratio, age structure (longevity within the area and range), local quality and population dynamics.

If these basic datum points are not clearly stated and quantified neither the ecological nor business management objectives can be formulated. In consequence *ad hoc* measures have to be resorted to, usually brimming with errors, costly both ecologically and economically and often leaving an aftermath difficult and laborious to correct. An example is the overpopulation of red deer in Scotland finding its roots in the appalling lack of understanding of population dynamics.

The general outline of the development of information has been variously discussed. We have covered the matter of counting and estimating numbers, evaluating the relationship between the overall numbers and the land range on which the deer live, and the rationale behind the population structure.

Population

We have also discussed the importance of population dynamics and the effect the population has on the feeding platform, as well as the necessity for numerical control to prevent the feeding platform being overgrazed to its ultimate destruction and devastating the ecosystem. Without this attempts at managing the habitat are bound to fail.

We can now look at the structure of business deer management.

Business Objectives in Deer Management

In the first place, it is probably necessary to put a business interpretation on the ecological objectives of deer management. Then we shall discuss, as well as highlighting, some of the 'fast practices' about which the owners and managers must be aware.

We have said that there are several possible basic objectives which may or may not be compatible with each other:

1. Containment or reduction of damage in the habitat.
2. Profitable management of deer as an exploitable asset within their habitat. Within this context managing for:
   a. venison
   b. sport
   c. trophies
3. Managing the primary crops with deer as the secondary crop.
4. Managing deer and the habitat for their protection and aesthetic value.

From earlier discussions it can be seen that management for venison, which calls for a female dominated sex ratio, is incompatible with the well-being of the woodland habitat and also does not lend itself to the development of sport or trophies. It is also inappropriate to the management of smaller species of deer. Management for deer conservation, too, is incompatible with any of the other objectives. It follows, therefore, that only hill deer (that is red deer and in some locations sika) may be the subject of a 'deer for venison' policy objective.

Objective Limitations

There are a few basic principles which have to be spelled out when objectives are being set. Here we are dealing with two sorts of objectives; ecological, those which are aimed at deer and their habitat, and business, those aimed at the management of the estate business and economic viability. In some respects the two groups go in tandem but there can be a conflict of interests when it comes to the size of business and business growth. Here the size of business is limited not only by the area of the deer range within the managed property, but also the number of deer that the property can economically and ecologically sustain. Consideration is being given here to the utilisation of the habitat as a feeding platform, the risk of damage (to other business interests such as agriculture and silviculture) and the quality of feed naturally provided by the habitat at the acceptable, tolerated, level of damage. This is where the value of damage is adequately compensated for by the revenue brought in by deer as a cost/profit centre.

Support and Exclusion – Habitat

We require objectives to be set so that we have a clear concept of why we manage deer (and to what end) and have some criteria by which to judge the achievements. However, we have to accept that there are some objectives which the habitat cannot support or which it limits and which therefore may be rendered less profitable, of doubtful value or may be impractical if not impossible to implement.

For instance there are some parts of the country where, inexplicably, some species of deer don't do well. Thetford Chase is one; in spite of the efforts of Forestry Commission staff and others it has never been known to have produced a good roe head. Therefore to manage Thetford for roe trophies would be impractical. Conversely, the area is famous for its red deer and setting high quality red deer trophies as an objective, especially in view of its supportive habitat, is feasible even though red deer numbers have to be kept low to prevent excessive damage to the surrounding forestry and agricultural interests.

Red deer need large complexes of forest. Isolated copses would not support red deer, which require terrain measured in thousands of acres and not tens. On the other hand a series of copses interspersed with farmland would present a supportive habitat for roe, and larger denser copses perhaps for fallow.

We have discussed at length the question of deer capacity in relation to the feeding potential. If a management objective calling for a very high deer population has been set in order to achieve an economic return this may be impossible to realise without significantly damaging, or even completely devastating, the habitat.

Although it may by now be obvious and should not need spelling out, managing deer in large dense conifer forests is not a practical proposition. In these forests deer live and survive mainly in the margins where light penetration allows some ground cover to develop. At best deer control may be exercised as damage protection until the day when landscaping and opening out the forest provides opportunities for better feeding and more efficient culling facilities.

Support and Exclusion – Species

Fallow and roe deer do not usually get on together. It is roe which are the sufferers so it would be impractical to try to manage them with fallow deer present and expect much success. It does not mean that if the two are present we should not try to derive some benefit from the roe.

Many areas are today being colonised by muntjac and in some, muntjac is the only species present. In other areas fallow, roe and possibly other deer share with muntjac. Roe and fallow are more likely than other species because they share a preference for a similar habitat.

Muntjac on their own are not suitable for viable economic management since the return they would bring from letting, from venison and from trophies would be insufficient. Furthermore, on account of their size, they lend themselves to no more than control culling. They do, however, present a limited opportunity for stalking lets, selling venison and for the trophy collector, alongside the more business viable management of the larger species.

Support and Exclusion – Business

The first issue is that of size. Deer management as a business must produce an economic return. A small farm woodland which holds and attracts a few pheasants or a roe buck and doe during the year may be a lot of fun for the owner, but it is not a viable manageable unit. Several such units might be, and a management group could be formed to jointly manage game and deer economically.

There are some deer which in the true sense of the word cannot be 'managed'. Muntjac and Chinese water deer are obvious examples for this group. Their very nature, habits and habitat are such that whilst they can be culled, the stalking let and the venison marketed, the maintenance of a rational age and sex structure, and density within set limits cannot be economically achieved. However, numerical control is important with regard to muntjac in areas where tree planting is taking place, especially in view of its breeding propensity and the risk of the rapid growth of the population.

Even the management of roe, which are much bigger and are far more widely distributed and of which we have much more experience, is regarded doubtfully by some people. Had it not been for the value of the stalking fees they attract (high quality of British heads attracting good trophy fees) and excellent venison (which, unlike red and fallow venison, is holding its value) they would have probably fallen by the wayside, in terms of proper management, just as muntjac and Chinese water deer have done.

In some instances business may demand that deer be managed in large numbers and have a high female ratio. These are situations where venison yield is a top consideration. The issues concerning risks and population dynamics have been discussed before. It is worth adding here, however, that the only situation in which such management can be contemplated is on the hill where culling is comparatively easy or in a park where venison production is usually a revenue supplement.

Under forest and woodland conditions a deer population with a high female ratio should never be contemplated and where it exists population reduction and a more balanced sex ratio should be major objectives. The risk of damage to the habitat from such a population is not acceptable in woodland.

Support and Exclusion – Resources

There is one final and important consideration – the resources.

Management of deer within an estate calls for a degree of know-how, not necessarily scientific but practical. The most important, as in many business enterprises, is the manpower resource.

The quality of employees dealing with deer is crucial. There is something unique in the make-up of deer stalkers, gamekeepers and river-keepers. We often say that they are 'the salt of the earth' and so they are. They need to be devoted to their job, which calls for all manner of effort and sacrifice. The often forgotten side of it is that the work to be done needs to be compatible not only with the knowledge and experience of those responsible, but also the size of the resource. Frequently one hears the comment that culling, stalking, feeding of game and control of vermin cannot be adequately carried out because there are not enough people to do it.

In looking after deer, game or fish, we are lucky; there are many keen sportsmen and wildlife addicts who willingly help if needed. Such help can often be gained free of charge, except for a little guidance, advice and goodwill on both sides. There are many amateur stalkers of very high calibre who would more than willingly help with the cull in exchange for free board and lodging for a few days of what is, to them, a holiday. This is a concept often scorned by professional stalkers and keepers.

A large number of deer calls for a high cull and the supervisors cannot expect the impossible from the manpower available. In the hind season in Scotland an experienced stalker, with the good backing of a retrieval vehicle, can bring home six hinds per day, in woodlands probably three or four. These animals need to be gralloched, cleaned, skinned and stored. There is a necessity therefore for a suitable larder–workroom, larder-storage room and possibly a freezer, with suitable equipment.

The estate must have a market opening for the venison or cold storage large enough to accumulate carcasses until they can be sold.

However keen, the stalker cannot be culling every day, if nothing else the weather may prevent it. Hence the cull progress plan should be drawn up with achievable numerical objectives in mind.

There are no recognised performance standards for stalkers, but there are estates and Deer Management Groups where a yearly cull of 500 hinds has been achieved with four stalkers.

Deer Damage in the Context of Business

Before we can start developing business thinking in deer management it is necessary to put the question of deer damage into perspective, since this can have a considerable influence in business planning.

In terms of estate economics it has to be accepted that some damage from deer is inevitable. Most of the conflict between deer and land use interests finds its roots in the deer population being at an excessive level. This is usually due to inadequate management effort in controlling density, forcing deer to seek food outside their natural habitat. The thrust of our effort must be directed at maintaining the deer population at a level at which damage is acceptable.

Field Crop Damage

Pastures, cereals and root crops are all subject to damage by deer.

Dr. Putman[3] suggests that the total area affected through grazing (by roe deer) in a cereal field may be in the region of 6%-30%. The effect on the crop yield depends on the timing. Usually cereal grazing happens when other grazing is in short supply, up until mid or late April. If grazing stops by late April crops recover by the plants tillering (producing side-growth). This means more crop bearing stems, but smaller ears – the combination of the two results in only a marginal loss of yield, as shown below (crop damage in late spring and harvesting in July):

Fig.65   SPRING/WINTER CEREALS
             SURVIVAL AFTER DAMAGE

	Spring Barley (1983)		Winter Wheat (1984)	
	Number of grain-bearing stems per sq m	Weight of unthreshed ears gr per sq m	Number of grain-bearing stems per sq m	Weight of unthreshed ears gr per sq m
Damaged by Roe (means)	787	493	330	780
Standard deviation	84.2	100.1	63.9	147.9
Undamaged	672	578	367	720
Standard deviation	113.1	136.7	65.8	123.3

These results are corroborated on the Continent where deer often have to rely for their 'comfortable' survival on crops of rye, barley and maize; the calculated loss of crops is 'planned in', and excesses are subject of compensation. The quantification of the value of crop damage is difficult because of fluctuations in price and quality.

This loss of crop may be insignificant when compared with damage caused by deer taking up residence in fields of cereal in early summer, a regrettable habit developed in the main by fallow and roe deer.

Damage to pastures is more a question of loss than actual 'damage' since what deer consume the domestic animals have lost. Deer are unable to close-crop a sward like sheep, a practice for which goats are famous. They probably do not crop as closely as cattle or horses. As a result much of the grazed vegetation recovers by developing compensating side growth as it does after farm animals grazing.

Damage sustained by roots, especially fields of sugar-beet by red deer, and damage to gardens, including market gardens and nurseries, by all deer can be devastating. Use of chemical or visual deterrents may be justified here. Particularly galling is the damage by deer who are 'raiders' from neighbouring woodlands, usually referred to in Scotland as marauders.

Currently it is not possible to put a meaningful value on the effects of damage in the field as discussed above. However, in an attempt to quantify and produce an approach which could be further developed, there is a costing comparison of deer and sheep in the Annex to this chapter. This comparison is a valid one in a hill situation where there may be an opportunity to remove deer and concentrate on sheep, or vice versa, in an attempt to conserve the habitat. Neither is the damage in the forest easily quantifiable without detailed data of the damage suffered. We are able, however, to put some global values on deer as contributors to the estate's economics, as presented in Chapter 3.2.

Damage to Woodlands

We have discussed the damage which deer can do to trees at various stages of tree development. In forest finance damage to a tree is often unfairly weighted. It is sometimes linked to, and valued at, replacement cost even though replacement after a certain stage is impractical or at least very costly. It is also sometimes linked to total loss of timber crop, even if total loss of timber does not occur.

The fact is that not all damage is 'terminal'. Only a proportion of trees in fact die as a result of damage and not all damage is deer damage. We have discussed the correlation between incidence of damage and deer density. We should not forget that through control of deer we can also control the rate of damage. It is appropriate here to focus on tree recovery because this has a significant bearing on the economics.

To begin with the damage can be slight to some coppice crops – hazel, willow and similar which, even when broken, stripped or frayed, are capable of regrowing new shoots and cropping may be no more than delayed.

It is the survival of trees after damage by deer that is often on the lips of foresters and is an issue discussed in these pages and in many other works dealing with deer and trees. Vast amounts of money are spent in this and other countries on damage prevention by a variety of methods aimed at least at decreasing damage, ideally at its elimination. Some space is devoted in this work to discussing the question 'Can income from deer compensate for losses attributable to deer damage?' and some answers are attempted. Surprisingly, neither in this country nor elsewhere has enough research been directed to the question of the capacity of the trees to survive damage, to recover from it – either aided by humans or unaided, or on minimising the effects on either quality or quantity of timber crop in order to reduce the financial losses. If such research has been done it does not seem to have been widely publicised.

One has to accept of course that this type of research is hampered by the need to study over generations of trees to provide meaningful results.

In some instances one hears or reads of damaged trees dying in one way or another. Some have the bark and the underlying cambial layer damaged around such a large proportion of the circumference that the tree dies above the damaged area and perhaps throws out side-shoots below. In other instances, the open wound, though not large enough to cause the immediate death of the tree by itself, becomes infected by fungi, insects and bacteria which may induce death or decay. If the tree survives, its growth may be retarded and show scars for the rest of its life. Often such damage reduces the commercial value of the tree, whilst the extent of the loss depends on the extent of the decay or disfiguration just as much as the ultimate utilisation of the timber. That trees can survive damage is beyond dispute; after all one can view brashing and pruning as the wounding of trees and they recover and thrive upon it.

All of us, observing trees in the forest, perhaps looking for damage as tell-tale signs of deer presence, have noticed new and old signs of deer browsing and fraying, the latter often showing as bare wood tissue which has dried on its surface and is being slowly covered or calloused over with a new layer of cambium and bark. The tree continues to grow, apparently not influenced to any great extent.

Following this line of thought – the recovery of trees after damage, Ueckerman is quoted in Chapter 1.4 in discussion of damage as related to density of deer. He asserts that damage to as many as 15% of trees is acceptable because a large proportion of damaged trees recover. It is unlikely that a person of Ueckerman's standing would have made such an assertion without substantial evidence or research, but alas, we have no details of either. In the same chapter, I relate my own observations of damage incidence, but these are mere observations and whilst they may be informative they lack the substance which controlled research would have.

Ueckerman's assertions are probably expressed in general terms; a lesser degree of damage which will disfigure timber is acceptable where timber is grown for high quality veneer production than where low grade timber for pulp is the crop.

There is, however, one source of information supported by evidence which points to a tree's ability to recover well after damage although it is rarely referred to either in this country or on the Continent. Steinhoff[27], a second and probably third generation *forstmeister*, showed from his own and his father's observations that trees have a high recovery capability after stripping damage provided that the wounds have not been affected by fungal or bacterial rots.

From the State forest which he controlled he sold large quantities of timber to local timber yards; the forest was a mixed one so the timber was from trees of several species. The forest was also famous for its red deer and they were famous for their inclination to strip! Steinhoff gained the co-operation of one of the yards processing his timber and they agreed to supply him with samples of randomly selected cross-sections of trunks which showed healed over evidence of stripping damage.

The cross-sections were taken at the height of about 130 to 150 cm above ground level. They indicated clearly the areas of damage which had recovered, allowing the tree to survive and mature. Even if the market value of the timber had been adversely affected a total loss was averted.

PLATE 9   TREE SURVIVAL AFTER DAMAGE

Left: Spruce aged about 75 years, which at the age of 25 years had been stripped at around 75% of circumference. (Age line picked.)

Top Right: 65 year old oak, damaged by stripping.

Bottom Right: 48 year old spruce which had been damaged at the age of 18 years, 25 years and 29 years and which grew from a two stem to a single trunk at the age of 30, both stems having suffered damage.

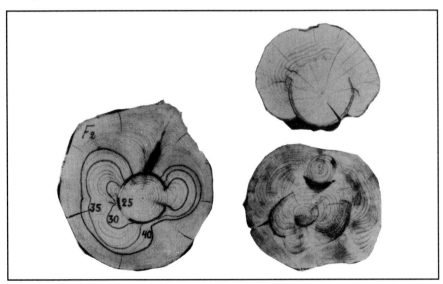

(by permission of DJV)

[27] Steinhoff, O., *Is Schalen immer so Schadlich?* in *Jagd und Hege in Aller Welt* (Heinzwolf Kolzig, Dusseldorf, 1957).

Annex to Chapter 3.1.

Deer versus Sheep and other Agricultural Income

Estate X as presented in "Deer Management"[15] and for comparison adjusted to current price/value structure. Sheep taken as a sample of 100 based on a 500 sheep flock; deer 1,589 red deer, sex ratio 1:1.5; culling 100 stags, 155 hinds and 33 calves.

Fig.66   INCOME FROM SHEEP

Sheep at values:		1974		1990[28]	
80% lambing	@ £4	£ 320	@ 15.20	£ 1,216	
100 fleeces	@ £1	£ 100	@ 2.18	£ 218	
Sheep subsidy	@ £1	£ 100	@ 10.31	£ 1,031	
		£ 520		£ 2,465	
Variable costs:					
Vet. etc. per head	40p	£ 40	2.65	£ 265	
Feed	25p	£ 25	5.63	£ 563	
Marketing and transport		£ 15		£ 73	
Replacements		£ 60		£ 136	
		£ 140		£ 1,037	
Shepherding		£ 200		£ 1,000	
		£ 340		£ 2,037	
Net income		£ 180		£ 428	
or per ewe		£ 1.80		£ 4.28	

[28] Based on *Farm Management Handbook* (Scottish Agricultural Colleges, 1991).

Fig.67   INCOME FROM DEER

Venison	at 1974 prices		at 1990 prices	
100 stags @ 140 lb	@ 17.5p	£ 2,450	@ 80p	£ 11,200
155 hinds @ 78 lb	@ 17.5p	£ 2,116	@ 80p	£ 9,672
33 calves @ 30 lb	@ 17.5p	£ 173	@ 80p	£ 792
		£ 4,739		£ 21,664
Stalking				
100 stags @ 20		£ 2,000	50% stags @ 150	£ 7,500
155 hinds @ 10		£ 1,550	no hinds let	—
		£ 3,550		£ 7,500
Gross income		£ 8,289		£ 29,164
Less manpower costs and overheads		£ 3,000	@ £50 per head	£ 12,750
Net income		£ 5,289		£ 16,414
or per head of deer		£ 3.33		£ 10.33

A comparison between the value of sheep and deer is difficult; parameters are incompatible and there is no accepted 'conversion' rate.

A conversion rate of three sheep to one red deer is used when a relationship is sought for the comparative impact on the feeding platform. If this rate is accepted, the removal of 500 sheep would allow for the addition of say 150 head of deer thus increasing by 10% the red deer generated income. Removal of 1,600 red deer however would allow for an additional 4,800 sheep generating a significant increase in income. How would such changes influence the hill vegetation, however?

As an extension to the sheep and venison costing comparison from Estate X above it is also possible to present the following equation (based on 1974 values):

$$\frac{33.33 \text{ (deer equiv. to 100 sheep)} \times £5,289 \text{ (net income from deer)}}{1589 \text{ (deer holding)}}$$
$$= £110.93 \text{ (net income from 100 sheep equivalent)}$$

The same equation at 1990 values = £344.29

These may be lower values than those generated by sheep but sheep values are sensitive to such influences as subsidies, compensation allowances or annual premiums, whilst deer values are taken at their lowest and without trophy premiums, which on good deer-quality estates could double the income.

The deer-sheep comparison is important because in so many areas deer and sheep are in competition with each other.

A wider comparison between deer and gross margins obtainable from other farming activities might be of interest but little direct use other than estimating the values of possible deer damage for comparison with loss of profit. Profit potential from woodland deer is discussed in the following chapter.

Comparing other farming income (per ha) would be very complex, space consuming and above all of doubtful value. The very variety of farming activities and intensities, large variations in land fertility from the Scottish Highland to the Lowlands, England and Wales and the complexity of measurement of agricultural performance and profitability would present an enormous number of possible permutations, on which the negative impact of deer upon agriculture could be evaluated. At the same time, a study of examples of income potential from managed deer in these situations suggests only a very marginal income, importantly hinging on the size and suitability of the deer woodland habitat, as a managed part of the total enterprise.

Deer income in the context of primarily arable farming operations must be considered, at the best, as no more than some compensation for damage, a small enhancement of annual revenue inflow, and an opportune by-product for only a small fixed cost. Above all, deer should be viewed in the context of them being a natural resource, an asset not acquired by investment, or competition for outlay of capital.

3.2. *Deer in Forest Economics*

THERE ARE two basic issues which have to be considered by anyone thinking of deer and woodland: the comparable economics of deer and forestry, and the influence that deer may have on year-to-year budgeting. The purpose of this chapter is to give an overview of these issues.

Economic Comparison

The calculations of economic comparison between forestry and deer are complex. Not only is there a multitude of variations which apply to each but there are also no accepted criteria on which comparisons can be based.

In the evaluation of forestry, there is a wide range of tree species, both conifers and broadleaves, with plant prices at the establishment stage varying from 6p per plant for Scots pine, 10p for some of the firs, 11p silver birch, and 60p poplar. They are planted at a variety of espacements, varying under currently prevalent practices between 2 m (6½ ft) and 8 m (26¼ ft) depending on species and to a degree on the owner's policy and preference. Then there is a range of maturation times from 15-20 years for cricket-bat willow, 25 years for poplar, 50-55 years Sitka spruce, 65 for Scots pine and over 100 years for some broadleaves. The complexity is further increased by the wide price differences for timber crops from say £10 per cubic metre to £600, depending not only on the species but also on age at harvesting and the quality of timber. But there are accepted planning, budgeting and accounting principles and adaptations to meet individual circumstances.

Evaluation of deer economics is a little simpler even though one has to contend with the fluctuations in the price of venison. Depression after Chernobyl shows how vulnerable to the unexpected venison prices can be. Competition from deer farming which, not being subject to statutory close seasons, provides venison throughout the year can also affect the market. The threat of proposed EC regulations concerning hygiene of 'wild' venison handling and preparation and competition from Eastern Europe may produce other pressures to venison marketing and pricing for which there are no established criteria. There are many inter-estate and inter-regional differences in the approach to policies and practices of

197

charging for stalking and trophies. The situation is an extremely fluid one and doesn't help to bring rhyme or reason to sensible comparative economics.

Fees for stalking are usually at a flat rate, either 'per head' or 'per day' (with or without limit on the number that can be shot in a day) and may or may not include overheads such as stalkers' services, transport and others. The differences are wide and moving slowly upwards with inflation. Trophy fees are often not charged at all (because of poor trophy quality? Or a lack of understanding of their value?); when charged, they are rarely raised on a sliding scale related to quality, because no standardised quality assessment has been developed for this purpose (some do use CIC scoring, which is laborious and open to some subjective judgement).

A rough study of charges (1990) shows the following:

Fig.68   AVERAGE STALKING CHARGES
                              (at 1990 prices)

	Red Deer	Fallow Deer	Roe Deer
Stalking 'per head'	£120–200	£100–200	£ 80–150
Stalking 'per day'*	£150–500	£120–400	£120–300
Trophy**	£ 0–1,000	£ 0–600	£ 0–400

* even wider differences may apply, depending on daily limits
** high fees apply to CIC medal trophies

Note:

   Some estates charge separately for stalkers' services, trophy preparation and mounting, vehicles and fuel.

The differences partly relate to the ability of estates to present and offer to clients quality trophies. Some are stricter than others in selection and in defining the numbers of beasts allowed under daily, weekly or longer arrangements.

In this very fluid and confusing situation it may be safest and most practical to approach the comparison by presenting a model which can be used by owners applying their own accounting variables.

Deer Management Model

Management of deer should produce an annual surplus from venison, stalking and trophy fees after covering running costs. This contrasts with the traditional methods, which usually call for owners' subsidies, even when excluding considerations of damage.

A yardstick for calculation of overheads on the Scottish hill, assuming that stalker manpower and associated costs are solely for deer, is £50 per head of deer per year. In woodland management, where deer and game are managed as a secondary enterprise and of the size used in the model

(1,000 ha with low deer density) it would be reasonable to apply the forester/gamekeeper/deerstalker concept. The deer-attributable cost element would be, therefore, about one-third of a fulltime deer stalker's costs and overheads, the other two-thirds being charged to keepering and forester costing.

Fig.69   ECONOMIC VALUE OF DEER

Basic Assumptions:

	Red Deer	Fallow Deer	Roe Deer
Area	1,000 ha	1,000 ha	1,000 ha
Deer density	1:33 ha	1:15 ha	1:10 ha
Population (50/50 m/f)	30	66	100
Cull as % of adult population	20%=3 m, 3 f	25%=8 m, 8 f	35%=17 m, 17 f
Venison yield male (m)	70 kg	50 kg	16 kg
female (f)	55 kg	40 kg	12 kg
Stalking male per beast	£175	£140	£120
female	–	–	–
Trophy fee average (per trophy)	£250	£200	£150
(Expectation of fee-worthy			
trophies 1 in 5 culled = 20%)	20%	20%	20%

Revenue Calculation:

	Red Deer	Fallow Deer	Roe Deer
Venison @ £1.70/kg			
male	£357	£680	£462
female	£280	£544	£347
Stalking	3x£175= £525	8x£140= £1,120	17x£120= £2,040
Trophies	3x20%x£250= £150	8x20%x£200= £320	17x20%x£150= £510
Revenue Income	£1,312	£2,664	£3,359
Less			
Share of overheads			
at one-third	30 deer £500	66 deer £1,100	100 deer £1,667
Net Income	£812	£1,564	£1,692
Income per ha	£0.81	£1.56	£1.69

Interesting information has been released recently by the management of the Forestry Commission's Kielder Forest[28]. The Forest of 60,000 ha holds something in the region of 7,500 head of roe deer, with an annual cull of 500 bucks and 500 does. Stalking is commercially let and venison sold. From that roe deer harvest, yields an annual revenue income of £62,000, or about £1.03 per ha of land.

Capital Value of Deer

When discussing the value of deer and forest, it is necessary to consider their respective capital values.

In the context of this work it has to be assumed that deer are a natural asset, they do not have to be 'installed' hence there is no initial outlay.

Over the last 25 years the capital value of deer in Scotland has undergone a dramatic change from £500 per stag in 1960, to £12,000 in 1987[29] and rising yearly, to over £15,000 in 1990. These values do not take into consideration the quality of stags, but we can look forward to a day when this quality will also have an influence on capital valuation.

The recent changes in values of deer as affecting the value of property are demonstrated by the value of a 20 stag forest which rose from £120,000 in 1985, to £500,000 by 1990 (over the same time-span a small in-hand farm with 750 ewes has moved in price from £100,000 to £200,000, a six-bedroomed shooting lodge from £80,000 to £200,000 and three cottages from £55,000 to £90,000).[30]

So far, the presence of fallow or roe deer has not shown a tendency to affect the valuation of property in any significant way, but the day when this happens cannot be far away, as game exploitation already influences valuations. It is also likely that valuations in England will follow.

Forestry Economics

The differences and wide margins which are applied by various authorities and individuals to the finance of forest planning are illustrated in the example on page 202, where the author has allowed a wide range of values to cater for a variety of tree species and the quality of timber. On top of this allowances have to be made for geographical differences, business and forestry accounting and trading practices. Furthermore, the revenues over the years of forest maturity are of little consequence unless these are discounted to year 0 (today), even the level of discounting is a matter of the owner's philosophy and choice, subject to national economics, business practice and opinion.

In these circumstances presenting costs and revenues becomes confusing, if not misleading. As a result a specific model has been developed for the calculation and presentation of comparative economics, allowing for coniferous and broadleaf woodland.

---

[29] Mellis, J., *Stalking Magazine* (January 1988).
[30] Rettie, A., *Stalking Magazine* (October 1990).

Fig.70　　　INCOME AND EXPENDITURE PROFILE –
FORESTRY

	Sitka Spruce Class 16 £/ha	Mixed Beech, Ash etc. £/ha
Fencing	900	—
Shelters and stakes	—	858
Establishment expenditure	505	1,080
	1,405	1,938
Income:		
Grants	795	1,375
Thinnings and felling	(year 58) 25,866	(year 80) 13,055
	26,661	14,430
Excess of income	25,256	12,492

Such calculations, however, have to be revised every time grants and other incentives are changed or introduced and the value of timber fluctuates. In the last decade we have had several grant schemes and an extract from these is included in Annex 2 to this chapter. The money yield per ha has also to be regarded as theoretical being at today's prices and not discounted over the period of maturity. Costs are also at today's prices and the two should not be offset against each other.

Value of Deer over the Period of Forest Maturity

The calculation of the value of deer can be developed as follows:

Assume that 50% of yearly income from deer (page 199) covers the revenue spent on deer management and the other 50% is invested every year at the same 5% as used in discount calculations for forestry.

Fig.71　　　　　LONG TERM VALUE OF DEER

	Red Deer £/ha	Fallow Deer £/ha	Roe Deer £/ha
Net income	0.81	1.56	1.59

50% of the above invested yearly at 5% at compound interest:

	Red Deer	Fallow Deer	Roe Deer
after 50 years/ha	£ 4,644	£ 8,944	£ 9,116
75 years/ha	£15,727	£30,289	£30,872

Capital Value of Forest

By comparison the current market values of forests are quoted by C.E. Hart[31] as follows:

Fig.72   LONG TERM VALUE OF FORESTRY

Conifers

Young plantations	1– 5 years	£/ha 600– 1,400
	8–15 years	1,000– 2,000
	12–20 years	1,500– 3,000
	20–25 years	2,500– 4,000

Conifers mixed with broadleaves

Middle age	2,500– 3,500
Maturing	4,000– 6,000
Mature	5,500–10,000

Broadleaves

Coppice, mixed species	1,000– 1,500
sweet chestnut	2,000– 2,500
Middle age	3,000– 4,000
Maturing	4,000– 7,000
Mature	7,000–15,000 plus

Deer in the Forestry Budget

In most well run businesses there is a need to budget, plan and set financial and other objectives. The budget, like other plans, can be short-term covering one financial year and long-term covering the specific development plan, in forestry from conception to felling. Forestry budgeting is also cast at five or ten yearly intervals, probably because this way it can be linked with periodic thinnings. In its concept the budget will show a significant capital investment in the early years, revenue expenditure in maintenance in the interim years and a significant return on capital invested in the cropping period. In relation to deer, such a long-term budget represents several generations of deer.

A forest planned with deer as a recognised product should reflect deer in its budget. It is not the intention here to show how the budget is structured because different organisations and accountants have different budgeting parameters and principles. The intention is, however, to highlight a few points which may merit consideration.

[31] Hart, C.E., *Private Woodland – a Guide* (Published Author, 1987).

Long-Term Budget

In the long-term budget, capital costs have to be included whether deer are there or not. Thus the establishment costs are not affected. Somewhere between establishment and cropping an allowance must be built-in for planting failures, and a proportion of these might be attributable to deer damage.

Yearly income from deer needs to be singled out against the costs of deer and some of these issues are discussed below.

Costs

1.   Manpower and equipment. It is unlikely that in forests, other than the very large, deer become so important and so 'time consuming' that they justify a separate cadre of employees and vehicles. Indeed, increasingly a combination of forester/stalker is being used, until recently with opposition on the grounds of traditional employment practices, although a stalker/gamekeeper seems an acceptable concept. Forester/stalker, or even forester/stalker/keeper, is an inviting proposition for it commits the employee to all three operations as an integrated effort. Importantly also the costs of each operation can be apportioned within the overall expenditure.

Costs Relating Solely to Deer

1.   Initial preparation of the feeding fields at the establishment stage, including cultivation, fertilising and seeding, will attract expenditure at agricultural rates, a maximum of £250 per ha at today's prices.
2.   If rides and forest margins are to be planted with shrubs and non-crop trees a small allowance needs to be made for these.
3.   Feeding fields need to be tended, and perhaps fertilised and reseeded from time to time. This could be performed by the forester/stalker. If the original seed mixture has been carefully selected there will be re-generation but if not annual reseeding at a cost in the order of £200 per ha could be necessary. Experience suggests that, all being well, reseeding will only be required every 5-10 years depending on soil conditions.
4.   Stalking paths require cleaning probably twice per year, so assuming that they work out at 100 m run per ha of forest at the cost agricultural equivalent of £15 per ha, the cost would run to one-fiftieth, that is 30p per ha of forest.

Savings

Against these 'deer specific costs' there are some small savings.

1.   The allowance for deer feeding fields 'saves' tree planting over 1% of the area.

2. The proportion of tree failures attributable to deer damage can be reduced. Forestry and estate managers allow between 5%-10% of area as an overall failure rate. The forest plan which allows for feeding fields, includes provision of shrubs and non-crop trees for fraying and threshing and maintains deer at a rational density should reduce the cost of damage by 50%.

Annex 1 to Chapter 3.2.

Woodland Costs

A. Coniferous Woodland Example

Consider an area of 5 ha to be established with Sitka spruce with an expected yield class of 16. The terrain and degree of exposure and elevation allow thinning. It is shallow peat over boulder clay with a minimal fence line to exclude deer. Assume the area is eligible for Grant Aid under the Woodland Grant Scheme. 10% of the area is taken by rides, roads and landscaping. (Costings below assume contract working and exclude cost of land and cost of capital).

Fig.73   CONIFER WOODLAND – INCOME/COST ABSTRACT

Establishment costs:	per 5 ha	per ha
Fence – 900 m deer fence @ £5 /m.	£ 4,500	
Ploughing draining	675	
Plants @ 2.1m espacement @ £63/1000	650	
Planting 10 mandays @ £80 per day	800	
Beating up (10% losses) Year 1 – say	200	
Chemical weeding grass/heather spotgun	200	
	£ 7,025	£1,405
WSG Grant to Year 10 £ 795/ha	3,975	£ 795
Net deficit	£ 3,050	£ 610

Income

(intermediate trimming SS YC 16 2.1 x 2.1m espacement)

Age	Mean Tree vol	vol/ha	£/m cu	per ha	
23	0.06	56	6.15	£ 344	
28	0.16	56	11.38	637	
33	0.31	56	16.80	1,052	
38	0.48	56	20.74	1,161	
43	0.67	56	22.49	1,259	
48	0.90	56	29.48	1,650	
53	1.16	45	30.30	1,363	
58 crop	1.56	575	32.00	18,400	£25,866
Excess of income					£25,256

B. Lowland Broadleaf Example

Consider an area of 1 ha to be established with 50% Beech, *var.* Rauli, 25% Ash and 25% Wild Cherry. Assume pure line mixture and use of tree shelters. The objective is to produce a final crop of Ash, with intermediate yields of turnery and planking with Beech coppice cut on a 12/15 year rotation for firewood. Good loam over chalk sub-soil. Initial spacing 3 x 3 m or 1,100 per ha. (All pricings exclude VAT, assume contract working and exclude cost of land and capital).

Fig.74   LOWLAND BROADLEAF WOODLAND - COSTING

Establishment costs:

1,100 Tree shelters and stakes	£ 858
Plants: 550 Beech	
225 Cherry	
225 Ash	£ 180
Planting etc	£ 350
Beating up – say	£ 50
Pruning esp cherry 3 stages	£ 350
	£ 1,788
Woodland Grant Scheme Grant to year 10	1,375
	£ 413

Income

Current prices (1990–Southern England) for all categories; standing sales.

Chilean Beech YC 14
Three coppice thinnings @ £40/ft cu.   £ 1,200

Age	Vol.mcu	£/m.cu		
Cherry				
25	10	£ 4.00	£ 40	
30	6	4.00	£ 24	
35	8	8.00	£ 64	
40	9	10.00	£ 90	
45	9	12.00	£ 108	
50	9	16.00	£ 144	
55	9	18.00	£ 162	
60	9	22.00	£ 198	
65	9	25.00	£ 225	
70	80	60.00	£ 4,800	
			£ 5,855	£ 5,855

Ash : Very similar in yield and value to Cherry. With Ash as final crop, felled at year 80   £ 6,000

	£13,055
Less Establishment Costs	413
Excess of income	£12,642

Values much enhanced if Cherry were of veneer quality with value up to £ 332 per ft cu.

Note:

Money values are all theoretical, quoted for crops 70 and 80 years hence at today's prices and not discounted.

Annex 2 to Chapter 3.2.

Forest Grant Schemes

Farm Woodland Scheme
(FWS introduced 1988)

Area (ha)	Conifers	Broadleaves	
	£/ha	£/ha	Payable in 3 instalments
1.0 – 2.9	505	1,375	Holdings between 3–40 ha
3.0 – 9.9	420	1,175	Annual payments £100-190 per ha
10.0 and over	240	975	for 10–14 yrs by woodland category.
			Planting grant non–taxable, annual
			grant taxable.

Woodland Grant Scheme
(WGS introduced 1988)

0.25 – 0.9	1,005	1,575	Payable in 3 instalments.
1.0 – 2.9	880	1,375	No Schedule D relief. 'Better land
3.0 – 9.9	795	1,175	supplement' one–off £200/ha is
10.0 and over	615	975	possible.

Forestry Grant Scheme
(FGS introduced 1981, revised 1985)

0.25 – 0.9	630	890	Payable in 2 instalments; Schedule
1.0 – 2.9	505	735	D relief available.
3.0 – 9.9	420	630	
10.0 and over	240	470	

Broadleaved Woodland Grant Scheme
(BWGS introduced 1985, revised 1987)

0.25 – 0.9	1,200	Payable in 3 instalments; Schedule
1.0 – 2.9	1,000	D relief available.
3.0 – 9.9	800	
10.0 and over	600	

Dedication Scheme

Planting Grant

	Basis I		Basis II
	110	conifers	145
		broadleaves	330

Management Grant per annum

	Basis I	Basis II
	£/ha	£/ha
		4.20
1st 40 ha	4.80	
2nd 40 ha	3.25	
balance	2.00	

3.3. Integration of Deer with Estate Business

O N MANY estates there are occupations which until recently have been seen as privileged. On horse estates it is the jockeys, followed by the grooms and stable staff, on fishing estates it is the gillies, riverkeepers and bailiffs, on shooting estates the gamekeepers and on stalking estates the professional stalkers. Indeed there were (and maybe still are) estates employing gillies, riverkeepers, gamekeepers and deerstalkers, each having and defending his own domain. Each has his perks, duties and responsibilites. They would have the ear of the owner, factor or agent, often because he knew less about their jobs and work skills than they did and would appreciate the existence of this skill to fill the knowledge gap. They often considered themselves 'badly done by' and underpaid, but rarely would admit to the value of the perks and tips which they invariably received during the season, and which no other estate employee was privileged to enjoy.

Closest to the hill stalker there may have been the pony-man and his ponies (a rare sight these days of motorised carcase retrieval) or perhaps the shepherd who might be told to move the sheep from that part of the ground to be stalked. With gamekeeping and riverkeeping there are similar 'supporting roles'.

In the 'good old days' of shooting, stalking and fishing those who participated were family and house guests, who valued the hospitality of the owner and the guiding role and advice of the employee in whose care they were partaking of the sport. Good advice and guidance were invariably rewarded by tips, sometimes very generous.

Times Have Changed

Estates where field sports are wholly kept in hand are few and far between. All activities of the estate have to be put on an economically viable business footing, with shooting, stalking and fishing being let and rented in a variety of ways. Even what is kept in hand for the family and friends is often accounted for by appropriate debits and credits to the house account and departmental account respectively. This change in the 'social' positioning of these sports and their subjugation to business requirements, rules and regulations has caused owners and their employees many a sleepless night in a search for acceptable financial, administrative and organisational solutions.

Employees

One of the first problems which has to be overcome is the traditional structure of jobs connected with stalking, shooting and fishing, *vis-à-vis* other jobs. Between the three sporting employee groups there is a feeling of superiority by each towards the other two. Many estates have grappled with the problem and have overcome it; in its wake a new breed of stalker/ keeper/gillie is establishing himself with the understanding that whichever component appears first represents the more important of the three roles (or the preferential role in the eye of the encumbent). In some instances there is a need for a financial incentive but on the whole the surgery of grafting together has been successfully accomplished. It also usually results in some manpower savings.

Where 'Sporting' is one combined departmental head and one cost/ profit centre, such job integration may be painless but in other cases where the integration has proceeded differently it has created problems. The integration under a microscope here is one of sporting with forestry. Stalking and game shooting is close to the forestry operation and it is not surprising that the forester/stalker/keeper is a possible job combination. Pure foresters tend to look askance at attempts to abolish existing trade barriers and fight against it. In today's employment market however, there is an increasing dislike of job demarcation and on the forest estates the integration of forester/stalker, maybe under the guise of forester/wildlife warden, is slowly gaining favour. Again some financial compensation may be needed.

The stalker/shepherd on the smaller hill sheep and deer estates can be similarly integrated. There may be a significant advantage from various view points in such a combination since, in his shepherd's guise, he can move the sheep either to prepare for the stalking season or to prevent overgrazing one locality to the detriment of the deer. He can also guide the stalking 'rifles' so as to avoid concentrations of sheep.

Administration and Accounting

In such integration of jobs it is important to maintain careful decentral- ised allocation in the administration of costs, incomes and overheads. In mixed sporting estates 'sporting' as a title may be dangerous, for it can hide high profits in one of the sporting activities and so benefit the less profitable ones. To this end, with integrated jobs, separation of costs and incomes should be observed. Some of these are obvious and easy, others, like wages, employee overheads and transport need to be split, usually in the ratio of estimated time utilisation and vehicle mileage, between each activity. Attempts to allocate cost on the basis of income generated is dangerous because again it provides camouflage for the least profitable one. The integration of forester and stalker or shepherd and stalker are good examples of where separation of costs is very important indeed.

In administration and accounting terms it may be necessary to buy out keepers' perks. Pluck, antlers, red deer tushes, skins and hooves are all commodities which are saleable and in fact are sold privately by the stalkers. They can represent a sizeable yearly income.

Many a gamekeeper has rabbiting as a perk. Also since before the popularity of deer stalking grew, he may have the right of deer control, especially in non-red deer areas. Today this could mean that he is allowed to take his guests, often paying ones, to stalk, sometimes even in the employer's working time; the stalking, venison, trophy, skin are the perks which may even appear in the contract of employment. Here the only hope is to buy these rights back from the employee or write them out on change of the encumbent.

Some estates letting shooting or stalking run a separate account for tips. They set a level of tips, collect them from the guests/tenants and distribute them between the keepers, the head keeper probably getting more than the others. This approach, unpopular with the keepers and stalkers, has the advantage of preventing unfair tipping cum bribing for the acquisition of a better trophy.

Administration and accounting for the 'house', family, guests, game and presents is sometimes tricky. A house guest shooting a prime trophy stag or buck costs the estate the value that a tenant would have had to pay. Many 'houses' accept this as a debit against the house account and credit to the departmental account. The same applies to game for the house and the guests.

Park Deer

When fashionable in the middle ages, deer parks were areas where deer, often walled-in or fenced, were hunted in all manner of ways. In the last century or two, hunting deer within the enclosed area of a park has been frowned upon as unsporting, even if it produces sometimes fabulous trophies. For these trophies some are prepared to surreptitiously take money from those who are prepared to equally surreptitiously shoot deer within the park. No one can even say that this is 'unethical' because park deer need to be culled to maintain the population at an acceptable level. It is not a matter here of sustaining the deer within the park on the feed that the park naturally provides. Park deer need to be fed because there are usually too many to survive otherwise.

Today, deer parks are an amenity for the visiting public who may be paying to visit the leisure or art facilities that the house and park offer. Deer are an added attraction for the public but are also a source of income through venison and live sales.

These deer having to be fenced, cared for and fed can and do cost a significant amount of money and, apart from contributing to the overall estate business by pulling in the public, they can be managed for a sizeable return. The deer numbers have to be controlled, deer therefore have to be culled or sold live.

Necessary deer culling in parks can be a difficult proposition. There are considerations of public safety, and of public reaction to deer being killed. Some parks therefore close to the public during the rut and for a few days of culling. They dispose of venison through gamedealers or sell venison from their own farmshops. Many sell deer live, having developed facilities for catching, tranquilizing and transporting them.

3.4. Where are we Going?

IF WE HOPE to develop a firmer footing for deer management we need to review some aspects of our approach to it. We have to accept that the sport which we have enjoyed for years needs to be commercially viable.

Stalking and Trophy Fees

Deer stalking as a business consideration within the overall parameter of sport is comparatively new. As such it still suffers 'birth pains' to this day. The question of values to be put on stalking fees or rents, trophy fees or premiums and other potential income within the control of the estate can be difficult to rationalise and even more so to enforce.

The difficulty lies in the method of 'handling' the family, friends and guests who, not long ago, stalked or shot basically for free. As times changed suggestions may have been made that they contribute something to offset the costs of 'running the sport'. 'Contribute' is an appropriate word because more often than not the activity was subsidised from the owner's pocket.

There are items of income which are outside the owners control; income from the sale of venison is usually through a dealer, who controls the market price with his fellow tradesmen. Whether it be for the venison export market or the internal market, the dealers handle the meat and dispose of it to private customers or commercial outlets. Hence here the owner is at the mercy of the agent or dealer.

Fees for stalking and trophies are a different matter. To a real sportsman it is the stalking that is the attraction and most are prepared to pay for it. After all, many travel abroad and others come from abroad, to get their stalking, shooting or fishing and usually pay through agents' fees which have been variously calculated to include owners' and agents' profits. Those travelling from the UK to other countries know that for 'the European big game' they normally have to pay for each head of game shot (sometimes even shot at or wounded), for local transport, accommodation, guides or stalkers, often calculated at overtime rates for early mornings and evenings, plus travel to the location and back. A premium for the quality of the trophy is also invariably charged abroad, ranging from nothing for a poor trophy to many hundreds of dollars, marks or pounds sterling for good class. In areas producing large trophies £1,000 - £3,000 for the trophy alone is not uncommon and the guiding factor usually is the CIC (Conseil International de la Chasse) score and there are no arguments! We have grown used to accepting the high fees charged abroad.

Sporting estates in this country usually handle their sport either through an agent or directly with the customer. In this they sometimes hit a dilemma. For example – a friend has been coming for many years. First he stalked for free and expected only to tip the stalker or keeper. Then he was asked to 'contribute' to the costs; with a slight look of a query he paid in good grace. In no way, however, has he ever paid for the real value of his sport, and the trophy was his with the owner's compliments if he wanted it. How does one handle this sensitive situation in the light of today's economic stringencies?

There are two dimensions to the estate's income from the sporting side of deer – stalking (the sport, exercise, countryside, company and all that) and the trophy – valuable to many and valued by some higher than the sport itself.

Maybe on some estates in Scotland and elsewhere, where trophies are poor, it would not be appropriate to charge anything for them, with the understanding that cull heads are within the price of stalking. A rare cullable good trophy head may be either a 'bonus' or be subject to individual and special agreement. But what is the 'value' of stalking?

A fee for stalking should not be difficult to calculate, whether on the basis of one outing, per head of deer shot daily or weekly stalking lets, with or without a limit of beasts to be shot. The keeper's/stalker's wages, overtime if appropriate, expected number of outings and their duration, and all overheads plus profit of say 25% or 30% as minimum, should be taken into account. Forests which are well known for trophies, amenities or other attractions, could demand an additional premium.

The trophy fee is a different issue. There is an increasing number of estates where for years, efforts have been made to improve the quality of deer by culling selectively, rationalising the deer population structure, and preserving the best to breed. These estates can now offer good trophies to their paying guests or clients. But the paying guests and clients, not just the family guests, in many instances have been 'spoilt' by being lucky and stalking at a cheap rate. Now, the owners feel awkward in asking for more, probably significantly more.

Can this be compared with life in commercial practice? There were times when family and friends were allowed all manner of perks from huge discounts to free presents. Times have changed however, and a percentage point discount may be all that is granted. This is even more strongly illustrated in other sports, many of which have lost or hidden their amateur status, becoming commercial and professional. Who would have dreamt a few decades ago that players competing in the Wimbledon Championships, or one of the famous Golf Championships would be paid, and earning vast prize money for being placed? Or that footballers are being paid salary plus goal premium? These are new phenomena in sport. Paying for stalking and the trophy is also a new phenomenon to the owner as well as guest or tenant. The game bird shooters and fishermen have somehow come to terms with this.

It is high time that the estate owners received a fair value for their stalking and the trophies and to this end, whilst not fixing prices, they should develop a new and more universal approach.

Charging for trophies can be a complex business. In some places trophy fees are established on the basis of CIC scores which is not easy and is time-consuming. But a method can easily be developed where fees are calculated on a pair of trophy attributes which are easily calculated, can be approximated when the beast is alive and assessed when it can be measured. Such attributes as length, number of tines, weight, spread, thickness, even beauty points would provide a number of possible 'pair permutations' and could be arranged in a matrix. Sensible sliding scales could be built into the two axes of the matrix moving in straight line progression, in steps, or exponentially in recognition of the trophy excellence. (See Annex to this chapter).

An argument often used in Scotland against charging is that the guests have to come a long way to shoot. Our sportsmen also have to travel a long way if they want to shoot in Bulgaria!

Venison

Earlier we said that venison price is usually outside the control of the estate. This need not necessarily be the case.

In the first place, subject to obtaining a licence to deal in game, estates could sell venison and game directly to the public. Many estates run farm shops where game and venison could be sold, with a far better profit margin than that obtained through the dealer.

There is however a much deeper issue involved here.

The entire concept of venison and game marketing needs to be explored and exploited in greater depth. The large supermarkets defend their stance against selling venison and game on the grounds that they cannot obtain a twelve month flow of these commodities. It is not quite as simple as this because they could deal with deer farms for 'off season' venison and with sporting estates for the 'in season' product. Also the argument does not stand scrutiny. All supermarkets deal in seasonal commodities, from fruit, flowers, and vegetables to seasonal food. Examples – cherries and other soft fruit are rarely sold in winter (other than frozen), leeks are rare in summer, and Christmas cakes other than three months before and a month after the festive season are unheard of.

The fact is that the internal venison market has a good potential which has not been exploited. Satisfied with the demand for venison and game from the Continent, we have done too little over the years to create a good internal market although some advertising has been seen recently in TV cooking programmes and competitions where venison and game figured surprisingly frequently.

And yet, in this era of careful eating, fat free diets, and organically grown food, what is more healthy and appropriate than venison from wild deer?

Maybe the lessons of Chernobyl a few years ago, and the slump in the venison market under competition from the other sources opening up, whether Eastern Europe or New Zealand, will trigger off a marketing drive!

Amenity

The drive for leisure is growing and with it the incursion of many people, legally or illegally, into areas where shooting takes place. This creates serious problems, not only of safety but also disturbance of the quarry.

On the whole a large cross-section of ramblers and walkers are good, decent people who love the countryside and fresh country air. Recognising their goodwill towards the country and the country owners, many owners have shown goodwill towards them by placing warnings about shooting taking place, maps showing where they may go and providing marked nature trails (where there are walls and fences) by building stiles, with a disclaimer in case of accidents.

The face of the countryside is changing under these pressures and it seems that the way ahead should be to try to develop a better understanding between the landowner and the visiting public.

Natural Wild Habitat Protection

All too rarely in the management of deer and game are we concerned about the conservation of the wildlife habitat. Farmers or foresters tend to be constantly concerned about damage to their crops, and damage which directly concerns their economic well-being. All of us, however, develop a very nonchalant, cavalier attitude to damage of the 'natural' habitat. In fairness, game management has more awareness of the necessity for a supportive structure of wild habitat, more so perhaps than in deer management. We have before us examples of this in some areas of the Scottish hills.

217

Because Nature provided both the ground cover of heathers, grasses and herbs and the deer, some of us forget that grazing pressure on the heather and other vegetation of the hill by deer and sheep, which may have sustained the animals, will sooner or later take its toll. We did not plant the heather, often we do not even notice that the colour of the hill changes. The heather, which a few years ago made the Scottish moor famous for its colour, is flowering less and less every year and in places it is no longer bearing flowers at all.

The purses of many estates have been hit, and many prides dented, when grouse numbers tumbled in recent decades. Much money has been spent on research as to the reasons why, but so often common sense has not prevailed and there has been inadequate resolve to take corrective action. In spite of warnings, not enough has been done by those in positions of authority or ownership to decrease grazing pressures to help and encourage heather and other vegetation to recover on the hill.

In an attempt to decrease the pressure, pleas have been made for years for significant increases in the red deer cull and a drastic decrease in deer and sheep populations. A few responded postively by doing so but too many shut their eyes and ears. All manner of excuses were presented as to why this could not be done, especially with deer – too few stalkers, poor venison price, more stags wanted for stalking, bad winter weather. So the number of mouths to feed grew and grew and are still growing.

As well as the heather, herbs and grasses the same applies to the few trees on the hill. However dwarf they may be, they not only suffer direct damage but are not allowed to regenerate, because whatever shoots from their roots or seeds is usually supple and nourishing, and becomes a magnetic attraction for the permanently hungry hill dwellers. (Recording of habitat damage – see Chapter 2.5).

The situation in woodland is perhaps marginally better. The foresters control their deer to protect the trees. At the same time they are able to protect the ground vegetation in these woodlands where it is able to revive and develop. In woodlands and forests where game shooting is conducted, the gamekeepers are very aware of the support their game requires from ground cover. Sometimes their efforts are negated by farmers, especially in smaller farm woodlands which are not grown commercially for timber, who occasionally turn out farm stock into the woodland to supplement their grazing. Of course the ground growth quickly disappears under such pressure, and indeed often so do the younger and weaker tree saplings and seedlings which are browsed, rubbed and ultimately broken by the foraging domestic animals.

We also do not consider the effect of other actions which we take on the wildlife habitat often enough.

To this day, the effects of fencing on wildlife and especially deer is not adequately understood. It is not only the fencing without downfalls which cuts across the paths of the habitual movements of deer creating havoc in their behavioural patterns. It is unfortunate perhaps that 'downfall' is a word coined primarily in Scotland and relating to the hills – downfalls are also needed on flat land when large areas of fenced-in land cut across the deer tracks and paths. Rabbit fencing is put up which deer get caught in and ultimately break, and electric sheep fencing is murderous to all deer who entangle their antlers. We have problems throughout the country with motorways which in some places cut right through movement lines of deer and other animals. We can build underground tunnels for frogs and toads, even for badgers and foxes – but for deer?

We even entice deer, especially roe and perhaps muntjac, to the roadside by planting tree cover along the banks and escarpments of roads and motorways but once they have been colonised by deer they will be a menace and serious danger to traffic. To add insult to injury we fence in some places and not in others. Sometimes the fences, of adequate construction, enclose the road, the trees and deer within, thus forcing the deer to remain in the proximity of traffic.

There are a multitude of operations which affect deer and other forms of wildlife. It stretches from taking over land for forestry, industrial expansion, lines of communication, which we all understand, to others which perhaps have a less obvious impact, like irrigation and drainage. It is not the water which these either produce or take away, but the change in vegetation which follows and which affects the behavioural patterns of the wildlife population in the affected areas.

It is encouraging to hear that when new roads are to be built or old ones upgraded, planning authorities will accept requests from landowners for the erection of deer fences in places where deer can become a hazard to traffic. These fences may or may not help the deer, depending where and how they are sited, but at least they will remove the stigma which surrounds traffic accidents caused by deer on the road. We have to educate the road planners, however, to ensure that they do realise that they have to allow for deer in their planning just as they would for people, farm stock, or small animals and reptiles who may benefit from narrow tunnels.

If only deer were smaller!

219

Annex to Chapter 3.4.

Trophy Charges

The following tables show possible approaches to trophy charges.

In choosing the attributes and the scales of progression it is useful to consult CIC scales (see Appendix E) and see which attributes are heavily weighted.

The choice of 'beauty points' (colour, pearling, symmetry, appearance) should be avoided as being subjective judgements.

Red Deer

Fig.75   TROPHY CHARGES MATRIX – RED DEER

Length or Weight		No of points							
cm	kg	7	8	9	10	11	12	13	14
50	2.50	0	25	30	50	75	100	125	175
55	2.75	0	30	36	60	90	120	150	210
60	3.00	0	36	43	72	108	152	180	252
65	3.25	0	43	52	86	130	172	216	302
70	3.50	0	52	62	104	155	208	259	362
75	3.75	0	62	75	124	187	248	311	435
80	4.00	0	75	89	150	224	300	373	522
85	4.25	0	89	107	178	269	356	448	627
90	4.50	0	107	129	214	322	428	537	752
95	4.75	0	129	155	258	387	516	645	903
100	5.00	0	155	186	310	464	620	774	1210

Notes:
1. There is NO link between the Length and Weight – either can be selected.
2. The vertical progression is at 1.2 rounded, it could be different, could be in steps or linear.
3. All three attributes could be arranged at different intervals.

Roe Deer

Fig.76   TROPHY CHARGES MATRIX – ROE DEER

Length   Weight in grammes

cm	300	350	400	450	475	500	525	550	525	550	575	600	635
160	20	24	30	40	45	55	65	75	85	95	105	125	135
165	22	26	33	44	49	60	71	82	93	104	115	137	148
170	24	29	36	48	54	66	79	91	103	115	126	151	163
175	27	32	40	54	60	73	86	100	113	126	138	166	179
180	29	35	44	58	66	81	95	110	124	138	151	182	196
185	32	39	48	64	72	88	105	121	137	153	155	200	216
190	39	46	58	78	87	106	125	145	164	183	186	240	259
195	46	56	70	92	104	127	151	174	197	219	223	288	311
200	56	67	83	112	125	153	181	209	236	263	268	346	373
205	67	80	100	134	150	183	217	250	284	316	321	415	448
210	80	96	120	160	180	220	260	300	340	379	385	498	538

Notes:

1. The progression in the vertical scale is 1.1 in the upper half and 1.2 in the lower half.

2. The weight starts in 50 g intervals and then is reduced to 25 g. There is no particular reason for this other than a personal preference.

3.5. Conduct

IN THIS section *safety* is taken for granted and it is not, therefore, included or even mentioned. Safety in using a firearm is a *sine qua non* and unsafe conduct must be totally condemned.

It is very difficult to lay down exhaustive rules of conduct, but there are some points which perhaps should be allowed space in this sort of book. To be fair, we need to address conduct to all who participate in stalking:

1. First must be the owner, his agent or manager since they either allow or let stalking.

2. Close to him the stalker, guide, warden or whatever his description; it could even be the owner himself or his agent. Whoever it is, there are some basic guidelines that have to be accepted and if it is an employee some additional rules apply.

3. Then there is the guest or stalking tenant.

The Owner or his Agent or Manager

1. In advertising stalking make sure that the advertisement is unambiguous. The prospective guest must understand how many animals he is allowed to cull, what are the quality criteria, what are the 'extras' to pay – trophy quality fees, stalker services, stalker's tips, transport, accommodation, daily routine, overtime payments. The same applies in dealings between the owner and a sporting agency.

2. The advertisement and certainly the agreement must spell out what can be expected. There is a vast difference between saying "two trophy stags may be shot during the season" and "you may be allowed to shoot two trophy stags".

3. Payment for wounding, missing and the method of assessing trophy fees must be explained before the contract is signed.

4. The guest or tenant must be in no doubt that the stalker-guide is in sole charge.

5. If a guest is invited, both he and the stalker guiding him must know precisely what the guest is entitled to shoot.

6. The stalker in whose care the tenant or guest stalks must have sufficient skill, not only in bringing the 'rifle' to a safe shot but, where a trophy fee is involved, in providing a reliable assessment of its value before the shot.

7. An employed stalker must be specifically instructed as to the number of animals and where relevant the number of trophies that a client can take.

8. As a tenant or sporting agent do not take out all the best beasts. Make sure that the principles of good deer management are followed at all times, and that the guests and tenants understand their deer management obligations.

9. As the 'organiser' make sure that the 'rifle' is an acceptable and safe shot, that his equipment is serviceable and he is acquainted with it, especially if he has had to borrow it. Ensure that the ammunition is acceptable and legal. The contract should include a clause concerning accuracy of shooting and the need to pass a trial shoot at a target.

As a Professional Guide

1. The professional guide or stalker taking a guest, paying or non-paying, may not accept payment for special 'considerations'. A stalker is duty bound to refuse, and to report the offer; a stalker accepting should be sacked, a guest or tenant making the offer should be asked to leave.

2. A guide, taking a 'rifle' subject to a trophy fee, must make sure that the 'rifle' understands the conditions, and that he understands any fee limitation stipulated by the 'rifle'. If the 'rifle' asks for the 'value' of a seen beast a clear best estimate should be given, and if a genuine error has been made, it should be accepted by the stalker in good grace – don't haggle when the beast is dead.

3. The guide must use his best effort to give the 'rifle' a good sporting opportunity for a shot at a cullable beast.

4. The guide should make sure that he guides at a pace which suits the 'rifle'.

Guest or Stalking Tenant

1. If you are taking on stalking with the view to managing deer on the ground, do not take on more stalking than you can satisfactorily complete. If you cannot complete your cull plan for reasons beyond your control, look for help, and advise the owner as soon as possible.

2. Always aim to cull selectively, unless you are faced with a vast reduction in numbers of deer.

3. Never take advantage of the fact that you may know more about deer than the owner does.

4. If, for whatever reason, for payment or for free, you are invited to take a 'trophy' don't be greedy – don't take The Best.

5. Always think of the conservation of deer when you cull or stalk for sport. Conservation must be our guiding light. Think of others, of next year, of the future generations.

6. If you know more about deer than the locals do, try to teach them, but be polite. Your aim should be to make them self-sufficient and to not need your help in culling; don't make yourself indispensable.

7. If you rent stalking, long or short term, don't feel that because you pay for it, you are entitled to take the best. The same applies if you let it; ensure that your sub-tenants know what they are allowed to cull. You should treat the deer the same way as a tenant as you would as a landowner.

8. As a guest or tenant you should not try to tip over-generously or bribe in the hope of being allowed an especially good trophy or for other privileges. If you do you should never be invited again and if the stalker accepts the bribe you may be the reason for his being sacked.

9. Taking the shot ethics are important. Shooting when not sure that the rifle shoots straight is not acceptable; you must check the zeroing before stalking, and agree to be tested. Next to it is taking a risky shot – too far, a moving animal, taking a longer shot than you are comfortable with. Taking a shot at your limit at dusk when in poor light gives a greater chance of inaccuracy and finding a dead animal is difficult and a wounded one often impossible.

10. If you are guided, shoot what the guide tells you and if you suspect an error of judgement say so, especially if you are offered too good a beast to shoot. If in doubt, ask.

11. If you spot a beast that needs shooting (especially wounded, sick or late rutting), speak up if accompanied, shoot it if alone.

12. If you are alone: (a) make sure that you do not get lost; (b) make sure you can retrieve what you shot or that the beast is well marked for finding; (c) make sure you are quite clear about the local 'dos and don'ts' as they apply to you.

13. We all make errors; if you have made one, own up to it immediately and honestly and apologise. The fact that you are forgiven is not a passport to another error.

14.   If you are a guest, make sure you know what to tip, over and under-tipping is wrong!

15.   Make sure that you are in possession of a current game licence, firearm certificate, adequate and legal ammunition.

16.   As a guest or tenant the same applies in reverse. If you have stated your limit and you have shot on stalker's advice within that limit, don't say "this one is not worth £ xxx".

Appendix A

Ballistics and Zeroing

BALLISTICS is a subject about which many enthusiasts become almost boring, the basics of which all who shoot must understand. These are as follows:

1. A bullet or any projectile fired more or less horizontally suffers a 'drop', being pulled down by the force of gravity. The drop depends on the weight of the bullet and its speed.

2. The line of flight of the bullet is called a trajectory – it is a curve. When we take aim, the straight line from the eye to the target is known as the line of aim. That line is higher above the barrel if we look through a mounted telescope, than it would be over open sights.

3. The trajectory usually cuts through the line of sight twice, once fairly close, about 25-50 m from the muzzle, the second at the distance for which the weapon has been zeroed, the point of aim.

Fig.77   BALLISTIC TRAJECTORY

Scope   Barrel   Trajectory   Target   L of sight

4. When firing at a target which is not at the distance for which the weapon was zeroed we have to adjust our aim. As the bullet flies above the line of sight in the first part of the trajectory (closer to zero point), we have to aim somewhat lower, below the point of aim and when firing beyond the zeroed distance we aim higher.

Fig.78 POINT OF AIM; UP-HILL
AND DOWN-HILL SHOTS

5. If we shoot up or down a steep hill, the bullet will hit higher than if fired horizontally. Additionally we need to adjust the point of aim as it appears on the body, firing lower when firing up hill and higher when firing down.

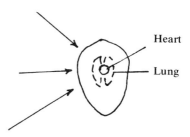

The Bullet

1. The sporting bullet which is allowed by law to be used on deer is one of expanding construction. This means that on impact the bullet 'explodes' and the bullet's core forces the jacket (the covering coat) to open up, possibly fragmenting, thus causing a greater wounding area.

2. The bullet leaves the muzzle at a speed described as 'muzzle velocity'. Under the force of air resistance the bullet's speed decreases. Bullet shape has much to do with the rate at which the speed drops.

3. The combination of 'muzzle velocity' and bullet weight is known as 'energy'. At the point of the muzzle it is 'muzzle energy', then energy decreases with distance until at the target it is 'terminal energy'. The relationship between the weight (m), which is constant for a given bullet, and the velocity (v), which is decreasing, is expressed by the formula:

$$E = \frac{m \times v^2}{2}$$

The greater the energy at the target the greater is the 'killing power' or effectiveness of the bullet.

4. Hence we speak of muzzle velocity and energy; velocity and energy at various distances. This information is provided by the manufacturers, usually on the ammunition packet.

Zeroing

Zeroing is making the bullet shot out of the rifle hit the target. Modern telescopic sights are constructed to make this as easy and simple as possible. The sequence of zeroing is as follows:

1. Decide on distance for zeroing (probably 75-100 m for woodland shooting, up to 200 m for open hill). Provide yourself with a firm rest at the firing point.

Fig.79   TELESCOPE/RIFLE
ZEROING

2. Fire three shots aiming precisely at the same point on the target, forming a group.

3. Select the point which is central for the group.

4. Take aim with the rifle at the original point of aim and using the elevation and windage knobs, move the aiming point of the telescope from the original point of aim, to the centre of the group. Do not move the rifle during this operation.

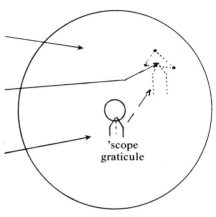

'scope
graticule

Note:

Most telescopes adjust by 1 'click' equalling ¼ inch at 100 m.

5. Fire a new group of three shots aiming at the point of aim. The group should be around the point of aim. If not, repeat steps 3 and 4.

Appendix B

Safety

I N FLYING, a cockpit check is a disciplined checking routine of all important functions and systems, through which the pilot and his crew go before take-off, before landing and on other occasions during the flight. It has been developed and applied because an omission to check could end in a disaster. In stalking, SAFETY demands such a routine. SAFETY with the weapon and ammunition, from the time they are taken out from the security of the gun safe to the time they are returned there.

Regrettably, there is no 'approved' safety drill like there is a cockpit drill. It is up to the stalker – professional or amateur, to develop his or her own and stick to it like a leech throughout the stalking life.

We shall attempt here to develop a logical sequence of checks which should be followed as the stalking sortie develops during the day, focussing on safety of the operation.

Preparation For the Sortie

1.   We must be sure that we have all the required equipment. Forgetting something that may seem trivial may lead to short-cuts which may be unsafe. Develop a check list.

2.   Having taken out the rifle and ammunition from a safe store, re-lock it. Check that the ammunition matches the rifle (there are ammunitions which whilst fitting into the chamber are not appropriate for the rifle –.308 will fit into .270 and will fire, both 7 mm and 8 mm x 57 look alike and the smaller will fit into the larger rifle. Some could be dangerous, others not work properly, finally some may not work at all). Check ammunition, it must be completely undamaged, especially the cases. A cracked case may cause a breech-burst.

At the same time check the rifle. Start with cleaning the oil out from the barrel and the chamber, check the safety mechanism for operation and the trigger pull; the firing pin should not protrude through the bolt face.

3.   If travelling by car remove the bolt from the rifle, store and secure rifle in the vehicle, keep bolt and ammunition separate from it. If you have to leave the car and rifle in it, keep the bolt and ammunition with you.

Never have a loaded weapon in a vehicle, even with the breech empty and bolt open.

Start of Stalk

4.   On arrival at the start of your stalk. Check the barrel for obstructions, if unsure of its cleanliness (must be oil-free) pull it through. Insert the bolt and check trigger pull and safety mechanism before loading. When satisfied, mount the telescope (unless it is a permanent fixture) and load the magazine (not the chamber). Always load the same number of cartridges in the magazine.

5.   Beginning of the stalk. On the hill with a stalker guide, the guide will expect to carry the rifle in its sleeve without a cartridge in the breech until he thinks the rifle should be loaded. He will either load a cartridge in or will ask for it to be done; safety ON.

In the woodland the rifle is normally carried fully loaded (cartridge in the breech, safety ON). Rifle carried on the sling over the shoulder pointing either straight up, or straight down (in front or behind the shoulder) – this is an individual handling preference. In bad weather the straight down position prevents rain/snow entering the barrel and you can safely put an inflatable balloon or other thin rubber over the muzzle if holding the rifle in up position. They are safe if shot is fired through them. (Note that the leather muzzle protectors must be taken off before the shot).

Whilst walking or stalking, check that the safety catch is ON, do this habitually and frequently since it can be brushed against twigs and be moved to the firing position.

6.   High seat. To climb into the high seat you should take the rifle off your shoulder, ideally unload it completely, certainly remove the cartridge from the breech. Reload only when you are safely and securely in the seat. Follow the same procedure when getting out of the seat.

On the Target

7.   When you have spotted the quarry decide how you are going to shoot; look for a secure rest. It may be a tree, a post, your stalking stick, or you may decide to shoot from your knee or lying down.

8.   Check the backstop. Never shoot at a target which has not got a solid backstop – to this end trees are no backstop, a bullet can ricochet from them and go for miles. The only backstop is solid ground.

Check for obstacles between you and the target – grass, twigs, any obstacle can deflect the bullet or even set it off.

9. If on the hill, only now load a cartridge into the chamber.

Throughout the preparation keep the safety ON and fingers OFF THE TRIGGER. If you suffer from 'buck fever', and many people do, breathe deeply – certainly do not attempt a free-hand shot even at a short range!

10. Only when you are taking aim should you take the safety catch OFF, when ready for a shot, place the finger on the trigger.

11. Immediately after the shot reload, in case you need to take a second shot. If there is no immediate need, turn safety ON. Wait for some minutes even if you think the beast is stone dead.

After the Shot

12. Approach the quarry with care, however dead it appears to be. If it does not move, first touch with your foot, then open the eyelid and watch for ANY reaction. If a *coup de grâce* is needed, fire at the neck or the heart, do not place the rifle too close to the body.

13. Before gralloching open the bolt, remove the cartridge from the breech and rest the rifle safely on the ground.
(Make sure your knife is razor sharp, blunt knives cause accidents).

14. Have you considered how you are taking the carcass home?
    a. If you need to collect your car, do NOT leave the rifle behind.
    b. If you drag the carcass, you need a good rope and ideally either a thick cloth or a couple of lashed branches to rest the carcass on so it does not get damaged.
    c. If you have to drag downhill, make sure that the carcass does not over-run you; on a steep hill it is better to let it slide in front, with you acting as a brake.
    d. If you carry it, make sure you know how to lift and shoulder it (if you have no bag or braces).
    e. If you carry in the hills, make sure you can cope with the weight without risking a fall.

15. Empty the magazine before you start the journey under 13 above.

On the Move

16. Invariably, we come to obstacles, from fences to rivers and streams. Before crossing, unload completely. If climbing over the fence lay the rifle unloaded with the bolt open, on the ground nearby (not under your big feet!).

17. Whenever you hand the rifle to anyone else, however experienced he or she may be, always remove the cartridge from the breech and open the bolt. The same applies if a rifle is handed over to you – don't automatically

accept the statement: "It's unloaded".

18.   If you need to release the spring tension always do it with the rifle fully unloaded and magazine empty, muzzle pointing at the ground.

AT ALL TIMES BE READY TO COPE WITH THE UNEXPECTED, FROM PEOPLE WHERE THEY OUGHT NOT TO BE, TO FAULTS IN THE RIFLE.   IF YOU HAVE A FAULT WHEN THE RIFLE IS LOADED, REMEMBER IT CAN FIRE UNEXPECTEDLY IF THE CARTRIDGE IS 'UP-THE-SPOUT'.

Appendix C

Disease

T HIS APPENDIX under the heading of 'Some Disorders of Red
Deer (*Cervus Elaphus*) in Scotland' has been prepared by
Dr. A. McDiarmid, D.Sc., Ph.D., M.R.C.V.S., F.R.C. Path., F.R.S.E. for the
second edition of *Wild Deer*[5]. It is here repeated with additions and
illustrations from the BDS 'Deer Disease Identification'[32]. BDS additions
are prefixed by *BDS*. The use of this material has been authorised by the
BDS Education and Training Committees. The text has been kindly re-
edited by Peter Dalton M.R.C.V.S., Hon. Vet. Adviser to BDS Wessex
Branch.

*   *   *

Introduction

Until comparatively recently the causes of death in deer have not been
systematically investigated and very little has been published. Most
records come from zoological collections where the animals are living
under abnormal conditions and are often kept well beyond the age to
which they survive in the wild. It appears that, on the whole, British deer
are remarkably healthy.

Accidents and Mortality

Accidents are common in all deer and most injuries are associated with
cars, snares (particularly those set for foxes), wire fences, nylon netting,
shotgun and to a lesser extent rifle wounds. It is a remarkable fact that
severe injury to the lower limbs does not necessarily lead to death.
Sometimes a whole foot may be lost and yet the stump heals successfully.
Broken legs heal well but with various degrees of distortion; infection
rarely becomes established even in severe complicated fractures.

[32] British Deer Society, *Deer Disease Identification* (BDS 1989).

233

Ectoparasites

The Warble Fly in deer (*Hypoderma diana*) is quite distinct from that affecting cattle and the presence of deer does not therefore impede any warble eradication scheme in cattle. Warble damage to deer skins in the south of England has not been recorded but red deer in Scotland are frequently badly affected.

BDS. The larvae much resemble the Nasal Bot Fly (opposite) to which they are closely related. The fly lays its eggs on the deer's coat in the summer. On hatching the larvae migrate to and rest in the deer's back near the spinal column. They emerge through the skin during the late winter and drop down into the soil to pupate. They are common in red deer in Scotland, can infect any deer species, but not other animals. They spoil the deer's skin and the appearance of the saddle joint. Sometimes badly infected deer can be identified by the marks on their coats where they have been biting at the parasite.

PLATE 10 WARBLE FLY LARVAE

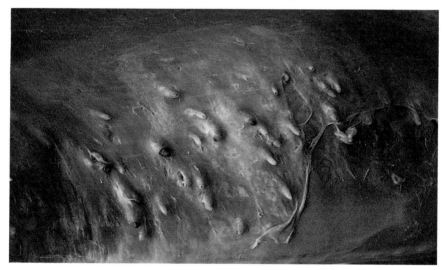

(photo by H.R. Rose)

The Nasal or Bot Fly (*Cephenomyia auribaris*) probably occurs in the southern counties of England and yet its presence in deer in those areas has never been proved. Deer have been observed exhibiting the characteristic signs associated with the presence of these flies. Red deer in the northern counties of Scotland seem to be the ones mainly affected.

BDS. These grub-like larvae look somewhat like deer warble fly larvae to which they are closely related, they are found in the nasal passages or the back of the throat of the infected deer. A badly infected animal may be seen repeatedly to lick its nose and to retch, but the parasite is not common in the UK. Infection is normally only discovered when preparing the trophy or removing the jaw for ageing.

PLATE 11   NASAL BOT FLY LARVAE

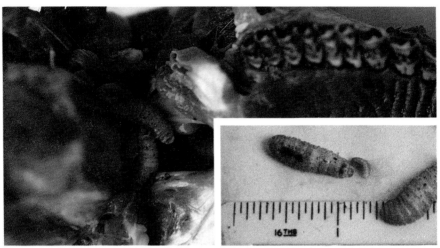

(photos by H.R. Rose)

The Head Fly (*Hydrotaea irritans*) can cause considerable distress in July and August in Scotland, especially to stags in velvet, and could be a contributing factor to their diminished food intake at this time of year.

Lice, particularly the biting louse (*Damalinia meyeri Taschenberg*), may be more common than we think. Few records are available but infestation seems to occur mainly in the spring after a hard winter, almost causing a premature moult in some animals.

The Deer Keds (*Lipoptena cervi*) are unusual insects widely distributed in most deer. They seem to be at their maximum concentration in midsummer. Very large numbers can have a debilitating effect.

The Tick (*Ixodes ricinus*) is probably the most important ectoparasite of deer. Hundreds may be present on one deer. Apart from the obvious damage they do in heavy concentrations on red deer calves, ticks are important vectors of disease such as tickborne fever, louping ill and redwater fever. Infection with tickborne fever is common in many deer herds but no clinical condition has, however, been attributed to this infection in deer.

BDS. There are a number of uncommon diseases and parasites which have less than clear sets of signs but which could infect deer, causing sickness or death. Some are blood diseases transferred by ticks and can only be detected or identified by full veterinary analysis of the deer's blood or tissue. Free living deer are more resistant than domestic stock to most diseases but can catch them, particularly if they have been transferred from one area to another, especially from non-tick areas, so have no natural immunity. Park and farmed deer might be vulnerable in this respect if they are subjected to an intense system of husbandry. One such disease is Louping Ill; another is Lyme Disease, which can also infect humans; medical advice should be sought if a tick bite becomes inflamed.

PLATE 12   TICK AND KED

(photos by H.R. Rose © Copyright MOD)

Endoparasites

So far as helminths (worm infestations) are concerned there is still very little known about these parasites in British deer. The vast majority of cervine helminths found in the intestinal tract are common to various species of deer and domestic animals. They are mostly *Trichostrongylus spp*, which is a worm parasite in the abomasum (particularly *T.aexi*). The worm burden is low in the small intestine and deer do not appear to be important reservoir hosts for these worms. Under natural conditions in the wild, the nematodes (strings) in the intestinal tract seem to be of little pathological importance, although problems arise under intensive park and farm conditions.

Hydatid cysts due to *Echinococcus granulosus* are, fortunately, extremely rare in all species.

Small Cysts(*Cysticercus tenuicollis*) are often found in the omentum and sometimes in the lungs and it is feasible that a fox/deer cycle operates in remote areas where dogs are not directly involved.

The two important helminths of deer are:
  a. Liver Fluke (*Fasciola hepatica*) and
  b. Lungworm (*Dictyocaulus sp.*)

Clinical disease due to Liver Fluke is rarely encountered except in roe. Red deer appear to have a basic resistance to the parasite. For example, in an area of Wester Ross where an attempt was made to establish a health profile of the red deer, sheep died in hundreds during one particular winter from *fascioliasis*. Despite this, red deer on the same ground showed only slight scarring of the liver and no clinical disease. In many deer no eggs were detected and if they were, they never exceeded 50 per g of faeces. Recent work in Canada confirmed that the white-tailed deer (*Odocoileus virginianus*) is also extremely resistant to experimental infection with *Fasciola hepatica*. One could argue that the behavioural pattern of the red deer on the hill takes them away from the infected snails at the time when they are most likely to be infective in midsummer. There can be little doubt that red are extremely resistant.

BDS. Liver Fluke. The surface of infected liver usually appears mottled. When cut open the bile ducts (tubes) in the liver have a thickened appearance often likened to old clay pipe stems. Careful examination may reveal the flukes themselves in the ducts – they have the appearance of rolled up, lozenge shaped leaves and are usually grey or light brown in colour. They are a common parasite of all herbivores grazing in damp areas, and in the state in which they are found in a deer's liver, they are not harmful to man or dogs, although they do spoil all or part of the liver for human consumption. Male deer with heavy fluke infestation may have deformed antlers.

PLATE 13   LIVER FLUKE

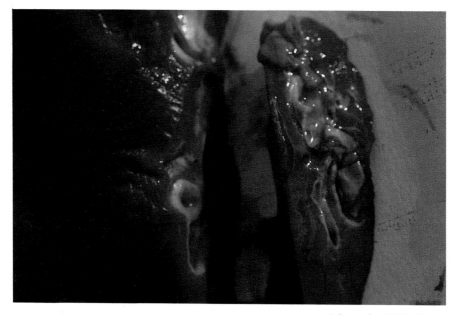

(photo by H.R. Rose)

Parasitic pneumonia due to Lung Worm. This is probably the worst disease of roe. Fallow and sika appear relatively resistant under free-living conditions, and red deer, although frequently infected, hardly ever exhibit clinical signs. So far as roe are concerned, the lungworm performs the same role in some areas that the liver fluke displays in others. Many roe under a year old die from parasitic pneumonia and when roe are confined in a small paddock this is always the principal cause of mortality.

BDS. Infected lungs show either light patches or greyish, dead looking areas, often close to the edges. Old damaged tissue sometimes appears dark, more like liver than lung tissue. If cut open the patches are solid rather than the normal spongy consistency. Worms may actually be found at certain times of the year within the lungs or in the windpipe where it divides into each lung. They do not pose a danger if lights are fed to dogs provided that they are properly cooked. The appearance of antlers of male deer with heavy worm infestation may be affected.

PLATE 14   LUNG WORM

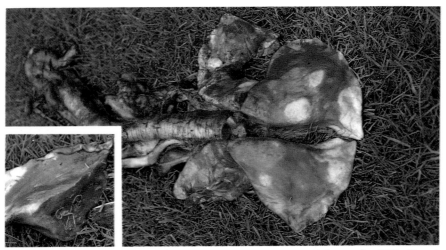

(photos by H.R. Rose)

Protozoal (parasite carried) Diseases

Redwater Fever has been found in red and roe deer (tick is the carrier) without obvious ill-health. Attempted transmission to bovine calves has failed. Recently the infection has been passed to captive red deer. It is probable that these *Babesia* are species-specific.

Rickettsial Infections

Tick-Borne Fever originally thought to be a rickettsial infection and now classified in the genus *Cytoecetes*, is common in all the main species of deer in tick-infested areas in the UK, without apparent clinical disease. The infection can readily be transmitted to cattle and sheep by experimental inoculation and it can cause abortion in these animals: susceptible deer from a non-tick area might well exhibit similar symptoms on their first meeting with the TBF agent.

Bacterial Diseases

Many of the superficial *pyogenic* (pus formations) conditions arise from mechanical contamination of wounds by bacteria such as *Corynebacterium pyogenes*; occasionally more deep-seated abscesses in joints and tendon sheaths are found. Sometimes *streptococcal* infections occur at the site of tick-bites but do not compare with the *staphylococcal* infection of hill lambs.

Brucellosis. Some serological evidence of this infection has been obtained in free-living deer in the south of England, but a more recent survey has not shown any evidence of antibody, or clinical disease, e.g. abortion.

Leptospirosis. Although common in a great variety of wildlife, cases of leptospirosis in deer are rare. Isolated cases have been found in roe and red deer.

Salmonellosis. This is virtually absent from deer. Only one strain of *S. dublin* has been isolated from a New Forest fallow in the UK despite an intensive search for such organisms over a period of many years.

Clostridial infections are also virtually non-existent. This is surprising when one considers the opportunities that red deer have for contracting the sheep diseases, such as brazy, pulpy kidney and lamb dysentery. Anthrax and tetanus have never been encountered even in areas where the incidence of such infections is high in this country.

Tuberculosis. About twenty years ago, several golden eagles were found dead or dying in the Cairngorm and Grampian mountains in Scotland. Post-mortem examinations confirmed these birds died from avian tuberculosis. Consequently, a detailed study was made of blue hares, grouse and ptarmigan to see if any of these could be a source of infection. All were free from tuberculosis. It was, of course, known that grallochs and carcasses of red deer dying naturally on the hill were also part of the eagle's diet.

Shortly afterwards, a stag was shot near Braemar. The inside of the abdomen and thorax were studded with white nodules. Microscopic examination revealed masses of tuberculosis organisms; tests confirmed these to be the Avian type. Tuberculosis in mammals can be caused by any of the three main types of tuberculosis bacilli, i.e. human, bovine or avian, and post-mortem findings can be virtually the same in some instances. The situation with regard to the golden eagles was now clear: it would be possible for them to contract infection from deer carcasses on the hill.

The question still remained as to how the deer became infected. The predatory birds were too few to cause any trouble. Deer will, however, eat cast antlers and the bones of their deceased relatives to supplement their meagre source of minerals.

Another feature of this form of tuberculosis is the effect on the antlers. They were very thin in the beam, light in weight and light in colour, all indicative of a serious metabolic disorder. Local stalkers had seen similar heads associated with poor-bodied stags. Several hundred 'normal' deer were examined, from different areas. By removing the lymph node at the junction of the small and large intestines it was possible to isolate a number of strains of the organism by culture. About 5% of all red deer examined yielded cultures – stags and hinds seemed equally affected without clinical disease necessarily being apparent.

Nine cases of clinical disease have been recorded in wild red deer in Scotland. Maybe the rigours of the Scottish climate, overstocking through bad management and the consequent lack of food all help to create a degree of stress so that the animals are more prone to disease.

Fortunately, human and bovine strains are rarely isolated from deer. Cases of both have occurred in the European Continent. In recent years four cases of bovine infection in roe and sika have been found in England near known infected badger sets. Unfortunately we still have a considerable amount of bovine infection by badgers, particularly in Cornwall, and it would not be prudent to set up deer farms anywhere near such infected areas.

BDS. Tuberculosis is very rarely found in wild deer. It will usually be seen as lumps in the lungs, or any other internal organ, or attached to the cavity

PLATE 15   TUBERCULOSIS

(photo by H.R. Rose)

240

of the carcase. These lumps are likely to be whitish or yellowish and if cut open have a gritty consistency. The disease is dangerous to man and dog if the raw meat were to be eaten, but is completely neutralised by proper cooking. An infected animal may appear to be in poor health but some cases show no sign at all of infection when alive.

Anyone finding suspicious looking nodules in a deer carcase should seek veterinary opinion before preparing it for the table or consigning it to the deep freeze. At the same time, 'piners' on deer forests should always be shot and, if at all possible, disposed of in such a way that other deer cannot gain access to them and thus perpetuate the infection.

Particular care is needed with all translocated deer and especially those imported from the Continent and escapees from deer farms.

Viruses

The distribution of viruses in British deer is not yet known. Fallow deer in Hampshire have shown evidence of mucosal disease antibodies but this is rare. Louping Ill virus has never been isolated from free-living deer in this country although a very high proportion of Scottish red deer carry antibodies, up to 40% in some areas, but no clinical cases have ever been recorded.

Foot-and-Mouth Disease. Free-living deer in Britain are susceptible to experimental foot-and-mouth disease to a varying degree ranging from a transient condition in the red to a severe form in roe. Fortunately deer have never been incriminated in natural outbreaks in this country although they have been found infected in the wild on the European Continent. Deer are also liable to become infected with rabies if the opportunity occurs and in recent years many cases have been notified in roe in France, Germany, Luxembourg, Belgium and Switzerland.

Malignant Catarrh. This infection is of significant importance so far as red deer are concerned. Originally African buffaloes were considered the main reservoir hosts, but sheep are now of greater significance, little or no clinical disease appearing in them although they are a potent source of the virus. One of the most interesting outbreaks ever recorded occurred in Père David deer (*E. davidianus*) at Whipsnade Zoo. The infection was readily transmitted to red deer and one of the interesting features was the long incubation period of up to 48 days. The disease then had a sudden onset, the animals were dull and had muco-purulent discharge from the eyes and nose, with considerable salivation. The source of the infection was never adequately explained. More recently, another small outbreak occurred in Scotland in a small group of red deer which had been moved into a paddock recently vacated by sheep. The first USA report concerned Axis deer (*Axis axis*) followed by other reports in white-tailed deer and mule deer (*Odocoileus hemionus*). Cases in sika were also recorded; these deer had been in close contact with sheep.

Appendix C

Tumours

Tumours are rare in free-living wildlife and deer are no exception. Lymph tumour (*Lymphosarcoma*) has occurred in roe and in fallow in southern England. A type of *fibroma* (skin tumours) which occurs in red deer in Scotland, appears to be identical histologically to the tumours described in the Virginian white-tailed deer in the USA.

Carcasses affected by malignant tumours must be rejected for human consumption; the parts containing benign tumours should be removed, the remainder being fit for consumption.

Swayback (*Enzootic ataxia*). Although not yet described in free-living deer, this disease is common in red deer confined to parks and because of the possible growth of deer farming enterprises, is worthy of comment here. The disease closely resembles swayback in sheep and is characterised by a bilateral demyelination of the tracts of the spinal chord. It has long been thought to be associated with a copper deficiency and appeared to be confined mainly to red deer. However, recently, cases have been seen in 'in contact' fallow. There can be no doubt that the affected animals suffer from a copper deficiency. Liver and blood analysis has shown this clearly but frequently 'in contact' normal animals in the same herd show normal levels. There is now some indication that the disease appears some years after the introduction of a new stag which may suggest a genetic factor. Under natural conditions it is extremely unlikely that a stag would serve his own progeny but this must frequently happen in an enclosed population. The disease is a fascinating one, not least for its close resemblance to multiple sclerosis in man; even the possibility of a 'slow virus' being involved is still under consideration.

Conclusion

The foregoing indicates that free-living deer in Britain, particularly the red deer on the Scottish hills, are remarkably healthy and pose little risks to 'in contact' farm livestock and man. The impression at the present time is that they have a basic resistance to disease which is far greater than that of the conventional farm animals and if this is proved correct they could become a valuable asset to our economy, quite apart from their sporting value.

When animals of any species are reared under intensive conditions the occurrences and patterns of disease change; this has already been observed in deer farms.

Note:
  Much other useful information will be found in Adams, J. & Dannatt, N., *Culling and Processing of Wild Deer* (Arun District Council and Forestry Commission, (1989)[33] and Alexander, T.L., (Ed), *Management and Disease of Deer* (Veterinary Deer Society, 1986)[34].

Appendix D

Law

1. Close Season dates for deer

	England & Wales	Scotland	N. Ireland	Eire
Red deer stags	1 May–31 Jul	21 Oct–30 Jun	1 May–31 Jul	1 Mar–31 Aug
Red deer hinds	1 Mar–31 Oct	16 Feb–20 Oct	1 Mar–31 Oct	1 Mar–31 Oct
Sika stags	1 May–31 Jul	21 Oct–30 Jun	1 May–31 Jul	1 Mar–31 Aug
Sika hinds	1 Mar–31 Oct	16 Feb–20 Oct	1 Mar–31 Oct	1 Mar–31 Oct

(Red/sika hybrids as above)

	England & Wales	Scotland	N. Ireland	Eire
Fallow bucks	1 May–31 Jul	1 May–31 Jul	1 May–31 Jul	1 Mar–31 Aug
Fallow does	1 Mar–31 Oct	16 Feb–20 Oct	1 Mar–31 Oct	1 Mar–31 Oct
Roe bucks	1 Nov–31 Mar	21 Oct–31 Mar		
Roe does	1 Mar–31 Oct	1 Apr–20 Oct		

Muntjac and Chinese Water Deer

> No legal close seasons. Recommended both sexes should be protected from 1 March–31 October.

2. Licences

Deer may be killed during the closed season only by the occupier of the land, or a person authorised by him, if it can be shown that serious damage has been and would be caused to crops, and growing timber.

Deer may be shot only by holders of a Licence to Kill Game but deer on the enclosed land may, however, be shot without a Game Licence by the land occupier or a person acting on his behalf.

Venison may be sold only to a licensed game dealer in England and Wales, or licensed venison dealer in Scotland.

243

3. *Weapons and Ammunition*

England and Wales

Rifles for use in deer shooting must be calibre .240 or greater, or develop muzzle energy of 1,700 foot-pounds and more.

Bullets must be of an expanding variety.

Airguns, air rifles, air pistols, arrows, spears or similar are illegal.

Shotguns may be used ONLY when authorised to do so in order to prevent serious damage to crops and growing timber. When a shotgun is authorised, it must be of 12 bore gauge and loaded only with a single non-spherical projectile weighing in excess of 350 grains, or pellets no smaller than AAA.

Scotland

There is no mention of rifle calibre in the Scottish Law.

The bullet must be soft-nosed. Bullets are defined only as : minimum 50 grain .222 Remington and muzzle velocity not less than 2,450 ft/sec AND muzzle energy of not less than 1,000 ft.lb only for roe deer; bullet not less than 100 grain .243 Winchester, muzzle velocity of 2,450 ft/sec and muzzle energy 1,750 ft.lb for all other deer. Shotguns may be used by the occupier of agricultural land or enclosed woodland (or a person authorised by him) to prevent serious damage to crops, pastures or trees. Shotguns must be 12 bore, and loaded as follows : either a single non-spherical projectile in excess of 380 grains, or a cartridge containing pellets not less that SSG for red deer, and AAA for roe deer.

Note:

This Appendix is intended as no more than a very general guide to the basic legislation affecting stalking. Every stalker MUST ensure that he/she knows and understands the Law in all its aspects, as it may affect him/her. The text of this work, or of this Appendix, may not be used therefore in defence in cases of breeches of legislation.

Appendix E

The International Measuring System (CIC)

THE INTERNATIONAL Measuring System[35] developed by the Conseil International de la Chasse is accepted throughout the world. In Britain there exists also a British method of measuring especially used in relation to red, fallow and roe deer.

The CIC provides an accurate estimation of the excellence of the trophy on the world scale. All measurements are taken in cm to an accuracy of 1 mm (0.1 cm), centimal points being rounded off as follows: 0.01 to 0.04 equals 0.00; 0.05 to 0.09 equals 0.1 cm; weights taken to 1 g (0.01 kg accuracy), and volume (for roe deer only) to 1 cc.

Trophies must be in a 'bare skull bone' and cut to the accepted standards as indicated below in *Fig.80*.

In many countries, and in some instances in Britain, trophy fees are charged in relation to the placement of trophies within the CIC scale.

Detailed instructions concerning measurements are in the reference. In this Appendix only the outline of the system applicable to the six British deer species is included.

Fig.80　　　　STANDARD SKULL CUTTING

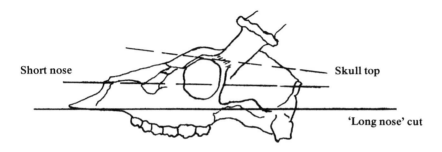

Short nose

Skull top

'Long nose' cut

[35] Whitehead, G.K. (Ed)., *The Game Trophies of the World* (P. Parey, Hamburg 1981).

Red Deer
Fig.81

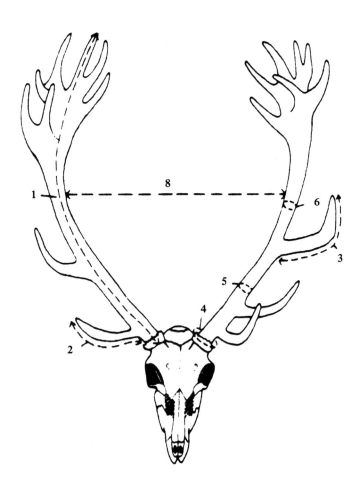

Fig.81   CIC MEASUREMENTS – RED DEER

	Measurement	Total	Average	Factor	Points
1. Length of main beam Left	.......cm				
		....	.......cm	× 0.5	....
Length of main beam Right	.......cm				
2. Length of brow tine Left	.......cm				
		....	.......cm	× 0.25	....
Length of brow tine Right	.......cm				
3. Length of tray tine Left	.......cm				
		....	.......cm	× 0.25	....
Length of tray tine Right	.......cm				
4. Circumference of coronet L	.......cm				
		....	.......cm		
Circumference of coronet R	.......cm				
5. Circumference–lower beam L	.......cm			× 1.0	....
Circumference–lower beam R	.......cm			× 1.0	....
6. Circumference–upper beam L	.......cm			× 1.0	....
Circumference–upper beam R	.......cm			× 1.0	....
7. Weight (dry) antlers	.......kg			× 2.0	....
8. Inside span (0 - 3 pts)	.......cm				....
9. Number of tine ends (1 tine end = 1 point)					....

Beauty points:

Colour (0–2 pts)   ....

Pearling (0–2 pts)   ....

Tine ends (0–2 pts)   ....

Bay tines (0–2 pts)   ....

Crown tines (0–10 pts)

Total	....

Deductions

FINAL SCORE	

Notes:
  1. Span points are based on spread formula as follows:
     (Span in cm x 100) : Average length in cm = %
     Points : 60% = 0 pts; 70-80% = 2 pts; over 80% = 3 pts
  2. Beauty points awarded with accuracy of 0.5 pts
  3. Deductions up to 3 pts for irregularities and lack of symmetry

Appendix E

Fallow Deer

Fig.82

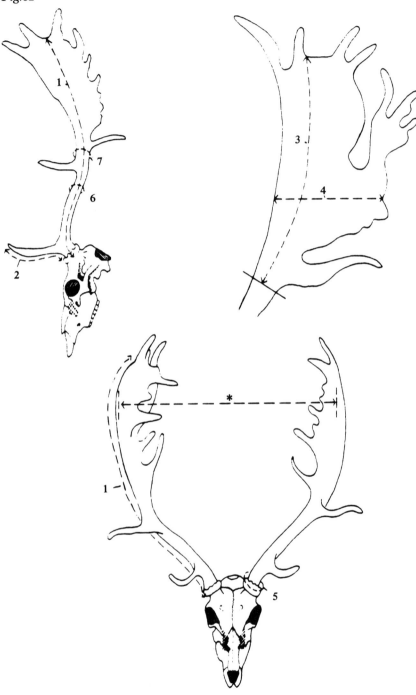

Fig.82   CIC MEASUREMENTS – FALLOW DEER

	Measurement	Total	Average	Factor	Points
1. Length of main beam Left	.......cm				
		....	.......cm	× 0.5	....
Length of main beam Right	.......cm				
2. Length of brow tine Left	.......cm				
		....	.......cm	× 0.25	....
Length of brow tine Right	.......cm				
3. Length of palm Left	.......cm				
		....	.......cm	× 1.0	....
Length of palm Right	.......cm				
4. Width of palm Left	.......cm				
		....	.......cm	× 1.5	....
Width of palm Right	.......cm				
5. Circumference of coronet L	.......cm				
		....	.......cm	× 1.0	....
Circumference of coronet R	.......cm				
6. Circumference–lower beam L	.......cm			× 1.0	....
Circumference–lower beam R	.......cm			× 1.0	....
7. Circumference–upper beam L	.......cm			× 1.0	....
Circumference–upper beam R	.......cm			× 1.0	....
8. Weight (dry) antlers	.......kg			× 2.0	....
Additions – Beauty points:					
Colour (0–2 pts)					....
Spellers (0–6 pts)					....
Formation regularity (0–5 pts)					
		Total			....
Deductions					
Insufficient span 0–6 pts)*					....
Defective palms (0–10 pts)					....
Edge of palm (0–2 pts)					....
Irregularities (0–6 pts)					
		FINAL SCORE			

Note:
Span points are based on spread formula as follows:
(Span* in cm x 100) : Average length in cm = %
Points (all penalties):
under 85% = 1 pt; under 80% = 2 pts; under 75% = 3 pts;
under 70% = 4 pts; under 65% = 5 pts; under 60% = 6 pts.

Appendix E

Sika Deer

Fig.83

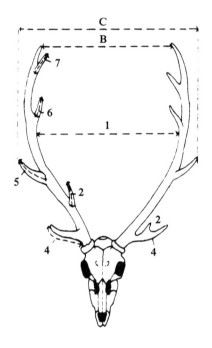

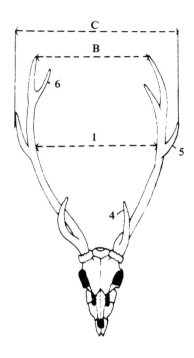

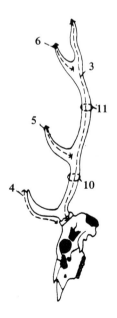

250

Fig.83

CIC MEASUREMENTS – SIKA DEER (non-hybridised)

Supplementary Data:

	Left	Right
A. Number of points	....	....
B. Tip to tip	..........cm	.......cm
C. Greatest spread	.............cm	

	1 Span credit	2 Left cm.	3 Right cm.	4 Difference
1. Inside span	....			....
2. Total length of all tines between brow and trey (col.4)				....
3. Length of main beam		....	....	....
4. Length of brow tine		....	....	....
5. Length of trey		....	....	....
6. Length of inner tine		....	....	....
7. Length of top fork tine		....	....	....
8/9. Length of extra fork tine		....	....	....
10. Circumference of lower beam		....	....	....
11. Circumference of upper beam		....	....	....
Total	....	....	....	....

Score :   Cols 1 + 2 + 3   less col 4   =   Total Score

....   = ... pts

Note:

Span measurement in excess of the length of the longer antler is entered in column 4.

Fig.84   CIC MEASUREMENTS – ROE DEER

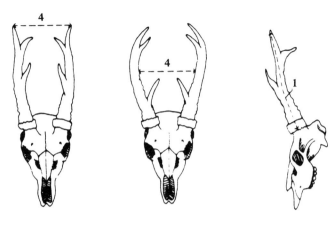

	Measurement	Total	Average	Factor	Points
1. Length of main beam Left	.......cm				
		....	.......cm	× 0.5	....
Length of main beam Right	.......cm				
2. Weight (dry) antlers	........gr			× 0.1	....
3. Volume of antlers	......ccm			× 0.3	....
4. Inside span (0-4 pts)					....
Additions – Beauty points:					
Colour (0–4 pts)					....
Pearling (0-4 pts)					....
Coronets (0-4 pts)					....
Tine ends (0-2 pts)					....
Regularity (0-5 pts)					....
		Total			....
Deductions (0-5 pts)					....
		FINAL SCORE			

Notes:
1. Span points are based on the formula as follows:
   (Span in cm x 100) : Average length in cm = %
   Points : under 30% = 0 pts; 30-34.9% = 1 pt; 35-39.9% = 2 pts;
   40-44.9% = 3 pts; 45% and over = 4 pts
2. Up to 5 points may be awarded for regularity including up to 2 pts for good tines.
3. Up to 5 points may be deducted for abnormalities including up to 2 points for short or missing tines.

Fig.85   CIC MEASUREMENTS – MUNTJAC

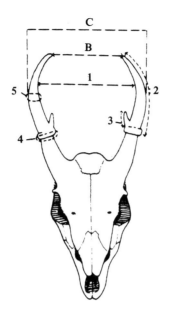

Supplementary Data:

	Left	Right
A. Number of points	....	....
B. Tip to tip	.............cm	
C. Greatest spread	.............cm	

	1 Span credit	2 Left cm.	3 Right cm.	4 Difference
1. Inside span between beams	........cm			
2. Length of main beam		....	....	....
3. Length of brow tine		....	....	....
4. Circumference of coronets		....	....	....
5. Circumference of antler at mid distance up beam		....	....	....
Total	....	....	....	....

Score :   Cols 1 + 2 + 3   Less col 4   =   Total Score

        ....   = ... pts

253

Appendix E

Fig.86 CIC MEASUREMENTS – CHINESE WATER DEER

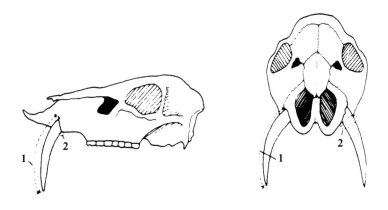

Formula:	1 Left	2 Right	3 Difference
1. Length of canine tooth	........mm	........mm	........mm
2. Circumference at point of eruption	........mm	........mm	........mm
Total	....	....	....

Columns 1 + 2   Minus Column 3

....   = FINAL SCORE ....

Appendix F

Carcass Handling

W E LIVE today in an age of changes. Some changes for the good, some for ill, others merely for the sake of bringing in something different. Many changes affect the handling of foodstuffs and hygiene. We have a phobia for covering everything with clingfilm – now we are told that clingfilm in contact with food may contaminate! But many changes are good changes and many are backed by legislation (or threat of legislation). Carcass handling is one of these.

That handling carcasses between the time of gralloch and the time of final sale to the consumer left much to be desired goes without saying. Dirty hands, contaminated ground, soiled knives, poor quality storage, delay on moving the carcass, they all contributed to growing concern. I suppose the day will come when the bird shooters will have to kill a bird cleanly with steel pellets (lead contaminates), make sure that the bird falls on clean ground, not into or near a cowpat covered with flies, that the dog bringing the bird has not eaten anything 'dirty' and so on.

But if we expect to persuade a discrimating public to change its habits and eat more venison, we must follow the principles of modern hygiene in handling carcasses, and be seen to be doing so. Behind the scenes we may bitch that the hygiene regulations or required standards, even if not 'regulated', make the life of stalkers 'impossible'. Impossible? Or more difficult?

In this appendix we follow the stalk and describe the activities recommended in current hygiene regulations. Stalkers should also be fully aware of the diseases of deer, as discussed in an earlier appendix, since disease recognition is an important component of the hygiene regulations.

The cardinal rule for stalkers is to examine all carcasses carefully, before and during the gralloch, even if the animal appeared perfectly normal before being culled. If anything out of the ordinary is found e.g. lumps, discolourations, swellings, deformed organs, place the gralloch and specimens in a plastic bag and take them to the nearest veterinary professional for a proper analysis. Make sure that:

a. if you bring the carcass home, place it where it cannot contaminate other food, out of reach of animals or people;

b. if you decide to leave it *insitu*, make sure that carrion eaters cannot reach it. It's best to bury it and mark the spot.

(You will find MAFF/DAFS Laboratory telephone numbers in the local telephone directory).

The commonest cause of death of wild deer is starvation. If the deer appeared in poor health, sick and emaciated, check the colour of the bone marrow. A red jelly-like appearance is an indication that the animal was close to starvation, having used up all the fat reserves in the marrow which make the marrow appear white.

You might well be advised to have with you the British Deer Society *Deer Disease Identification* for a quick (and weather proof) identification or memory refresher!

*   *   *

The beast has been killed with a nice clean shot! The stalker and the guide stand over it ready to start gralloching (gutting).

1. Turn the beast on its back with legs splayed (if possible), take out your *gralloching knife*.

Note:
   The gralloching knife should ideally have two blades and a bone saw. The blades should be one pointed, the other with blunted end. Blades must be razor sharp, so carry a honing stone or steel with you). The new type of knife has a plastic bonded handle, non folding (therefore you may need two and a saw).

2. Put on *protective gloves*.

3. Slit the throat lengthwise, from the top of the breast-bone well up the throat, expose the windpipe and gullet tube (food duct). Cut the gullet tube at the throat end, clean off flesh and tie a knot in it to stop any discharge of food into the carcass. Cut the windpipe at the throat end. If the shot was such that there was not much bleeding cut the main blood vessels in the neck and bleed (usually not necessary, the bullet would have caused adequate bleeding).

4. Pinch the skin about middle of the belly, and slit the skin making sure you do not damage the stomach sack. Insert the middle and fore-finger into the slit with the knife blade between them and slit, first to the breast bone, then backwards through the crutch almost to the anus, avoiding the penis sheath and ensuring that urinal duct and bladder are not damaged. Cut close round the anus in a circle to free the anus, for removal through the stomach cavity.

5. Remove the stomach and intestines: grip the gut at the pelvis and pull out ensuring that no faeces fall into the stomach cavity. Cut around the male genitalia and pull them backwards and out. The easy way is to cut the abdominal wall, and pull at the windpipe, drawing out the lungs, heart, liver, stomach and intestines. The hygiene inspection requirements are, however, that the lungs, heart and liver should be left attached to the carcass for later examination.

Notes:
1. From now on, be alive to ANY abnormalities in the organs. They are described and illustrated in Appendix C 'Disease'. You are not expected to be a vet so if in doubt, you MUST call veterinary or professional assistance to identify the abnormality and decide whether the carcass is fit for human consumption.
2. If you handle a large number of carcasses which are sold, you must be acquainted with the UK and EC hygiene regulations.
3. If you gralloch in the field bury the gralloch.

6. Turn the carcass on its stomach, splay the legs and allow the blood to drain. In preparation for transport clean out the stomach cavity with clean grass. If heart, lungs etc., have been taken out place them in a *clean polythene bag* for inspection.

7. Clean your knives and saw, remove protective gloves.

To remove the carcass

8. Roe deer and small deer can be carried in a suitably *lined rucksack or harness*, larger deer have to be dragged unless the vehicle can be brought to the carcass.

9. If dragging, ideally you should use a *ground sheet with ropes*. It slides more easily and partially protects the carcass from damage.

10. In the vehicle place the carcass in a *clean tray. Label* the carcass and the bag with offal for identification. Wash your tools and hands, (*water container, possibly disinfectant, first aid kit*).

Note:
If for any reason you have to leave the carcass for any length of time, hang it head down and insert a stick between the walls of the cavity to ensure ventilation. If you cannot hang and there are no sticks, lay the carcass cavity down with splayed legs.

At the Larder – Larder Construction

The specifications herein apply to larders which handle a number of deer, hence it is not expected that an amateur stalker would HAVE to comply to store a few carcasses during the year. There is no 'specification' which is legally enforceable at the moment, but where deer are being sold in numbers their storage may be subject to inspection.

1. The deer larder should be of a size which will allow the free hanging of carcasses of deer culled, without the carcasses touching each other. The larder can be used for game.

2. The area must be well ventilated near the ceiling with fly proofed windows or other means of ventilation. Walls and roofs should be shaded from sunshine to stop overheating. The perimeter should be fenced to prevent dogs from entering.

3. The services within the larder:

a. Water mains, with hose, wash basin, double sink with hot and cold water.
b. Larder should be connected to sewerage system but advice should be obtained from the council and local water authority to determine their ability to treat effluent with blood, fat, flesh etc.
c. The building should be in brick or concrete, with solid flooring. The walls and flooring should ideally be tiled. All walls should be coved. The floor should have a good fall to a water drain and have a non-slip finish. If walls and floors are not tiled they must be finished in paint of a strong washable variety.
d. Doors should be self-closing with a fly protection screen.
e. Lighting should be adequate for work without eye strain.
f. All equipment, tables, cradles, hoists must be easily cleaned, non absorbent (not raw timber finish) and not affected by detergents or disinfectants.
g. There should be either access to sterilising facilities for equipment or sterilisers should be installed.
h. Carcasses should be chilled at a temperature of $7\,^{\circ}$C or lower. Freezing should be at temperature of $-12\,^{\circ}$C in a separate freezer storage.

Staff using the Larder, should have adequate facilities for personal hygiene and first aid. The larder should have a stock of implements like knives (plastic bonded handles), saws, sharpening tools, identification labels (or approved tags) for carcass identification, writing material, weighing machine and record books.

(Much useful guidance will also be found in Adams and Dannatt, *The Culling and Processing of Wild Deer* (Arun District Council and Forestry Commission 1989).

References

1. de Nahlik, A.J., *Wild Deer* (Faber & Faber, 1959).
2. Chapman, Norma, *Deer* (Whittet Books, 1991).
3. Putman, Dr. Rory, *The Natural History of Deer* (C. Helm, 1988).
4. Szukiel, E., *Defence Against Stripping* (Acta Teriologica Vol.26, IBL Warsaw, 1981).
5. de Nahlik, A.J., *Wild Deer* (2nd Edition, Ashford Press, 1987).
6. Mottl, S., *A Case Against Damage by Deer* (Biologia, Prague, 1957).
7. Nature Conservancy Council, *Annual Report 1971* (HMSO).
8. Lindeman, W., *Zeitschrift fur Weltforstwissenschaft* (Munich, 1968).
9. Ratcliffe, Dr. P., *Deer in Upland Forest* (FC Bulletin 1971, HMSO).
10. Wagenknecht, Dr. E., *Rotwild* (Neuman Neudam, Berlin, 1981).
11. Ueckerman, Dr., *Wildstand Bewirtschaftung und Wildschaden Verhuttung beim Rotwild* (P. Parey, Hamburg, 1960).
12. Clutton Brock, Dr. T.H. and others, *Red Deer in the Highlands* (BSP Professional Books, 1989).
13. Muller Using, *Grundlagen moderner Jagdwirtschaft* (Kroger, Hamburg, 1949).
14. Fletcher, Dr. J., *Suggestions for Deer Park Managers from Deer Farmer* (BDS Symposium, 1988).
15. de Nahlik, A.J., *Deer Management* (David & Charles, 1974).
16. Lowe, V.P., *Teeth as indication of age* (Journal of Zoo No.152).
17. Mitchell, Dr. B., *Determination of age in Scottish red deer from layers of dental cement* (Journal of Animal Ecology No.36, & RDC).
18. Red Deer Commission, *Red Deer Management* (HMSO, 1981. Contribution by Dr. B. Mitchell).
19. Bubenik, A., *Das Geweih* (P. Parey Verlag, Hamburg, 1966).
20. Prior, R., *Shooting Times* (September 1991).
21. *Forest and Conservation* (FC Environmental Leaflet, 1989, HMSO).
22. Hart, C., *Practical Forestry* (Allan Sutton, 1991).
23. Red Deer Commission, *Annual Report 1986* (HMSO, 1988).
24. Prior, R., *Trees and Deer* (Batsford, 1983).
24b. Dzieciolowski, R., *Diet of European Red Deer* (Polish Ecol. Studies 2; 33-50, & IBL 365).
25. Pepper, W. & Lee, L., *Forest Fencing* (FC Pamphlet 80, HMSO, 1988).

26. McIntosh, Dr. R., British Deer Society AGM, 1991 and *Roe Deer Management* (Deer, November 1991).
27. Steinhoff, O., *Is Schalen immer so Schadlich? in Jagd und Hege in Aller Welt* (Heinzwolf Kolzig, Dusseldorf, 1957).
28. *Farm Management Handbook* (Scottish Agricultural Colleges, 1991).
29. Mellis, J., *Stalking Magazine* (January 1988).
30. Rettie, A., *Stalking Magazine* (October 1990).
31. Hart, C.E., *Private Woodland – a Guide* (Published Author, 1987).
32. British Deer Society *Deer Disease Identification* (BDS, 1989).
33. Adams, J. & Dannatt, N., *Culling and Processing of Wild Deer* (Arun District Council and Forestry Commission, 1989).
34. Alexander, T.L. (Ed), *Management and Disease of Deer* (Veterinary Deer Society, 1986).
35. Whitehead, G.K. (Ed), *The Game Trophies of the World* (P. Parey, Hamburg, 1981).

Further Reading

Brander, M., *Deer Stalking in Britain* (The Sportsmen's Press, 1986).
Chaplin, R.E., *Deer* (Blandford Press, 1977).
Chapman, N. & D., *Fallow Deer* (Forestry Commission HMSO, 1982).
Clutton Brock et al, *Red Deer Behaviour and Ecology* (Edinburgh University Press, 1982).
Marshall Ball, R., *The Sporting Rifle* (Pelham Books, 1986).
Parker and Thornley, *Fair Game* (Pelham Books, 1987).
Prior, R., *Deer Management in Small Woodlands* (Game Conservancy, 1987).
Prior, R., *Modern Roe Stalking* (Tideline Books, 1985).
Prior, R., *Roe Stalking* (Game Conservancy, 1987).
Waterton, H.A., *Going to the Hill* (Nelson, 1987).
Whitehead, G.K., *Deer and Their Management* (Country Life, 1950).
Whitehead, G.K., *Practical Deer Stalking* (Constable, 1986).

Annual Reports, *Red Deer Commission* (HMSO Yearly Publication).

Field Guide to British Deer (Blackwell Scientific Publications for British Deer Society 1971 and 1982).
Wildlife Ranger's Handbook (Forestry Commission, 1985).

Non-British:

Dziegielewski, S., *Jelen* (PWRiL, Warsaw 1970).
Frevert, W., *Die Futterung des Rotwildes* (P. Parey, Hamburg, 1956).
Heck, L., *Der Rothirsch* (P. Parey, Hamburg, 1956).
Lotze, K., *Das Ansprechen des Hirsches* (M. & H. Schaper, Hannover, 1950).
Pielewski, Z., *Sarna* (PWRiL, Warsaw, 1970).
Raesefeld von, F., *Das Rehwild* (P. Parey, Hamburg, 1956, 1985).
Raesefeld von, F., *Das Rotwild* (P. Parey, Hamburg, 1957).
Rue, L-L. III., *The Deer of North America* (Crown, N-Y, 1978).
Sartorius, B., *Das Ansprechen des Rehwildes* (M. Schaper, Hannover, 1950).
Schmidt and Gilbert (Ed), *Big Game of North America* (Stackpole, 1978).

Further Reading

Ueckerman, E., *Das Damwild* (P. Parey, Hamburg, 1956).

Lehrbuch Jaegerprufung, Vol. 1-5 (P. Parey, Hamburg, 1980).

Periodicals:

The Field
Field Sports and Conservation
Deer
Shooting Times
Stalking Magazine

Index

Index